We Celebrate Together

Happy Birthday

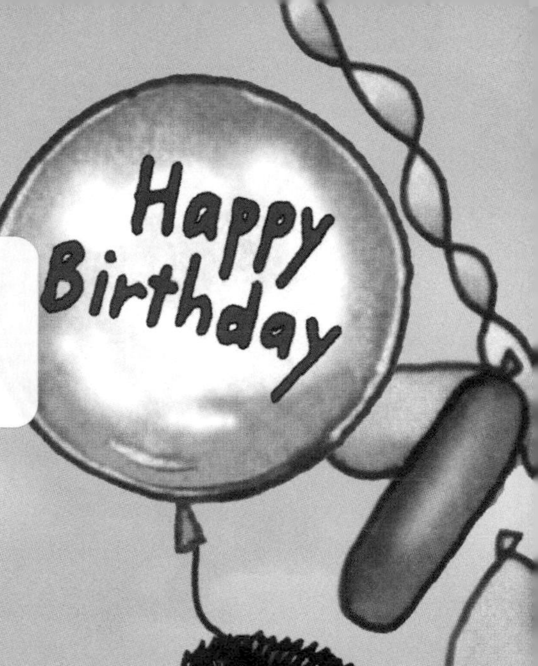

This Week's Scripture

speaks about the importance of special family celebrations.

Happy Families

There, too, before the LORD, your God, you and your families shall eat and make merry, because the LORD, your God, has blessed you.

Based on Deuteronomy 12:7

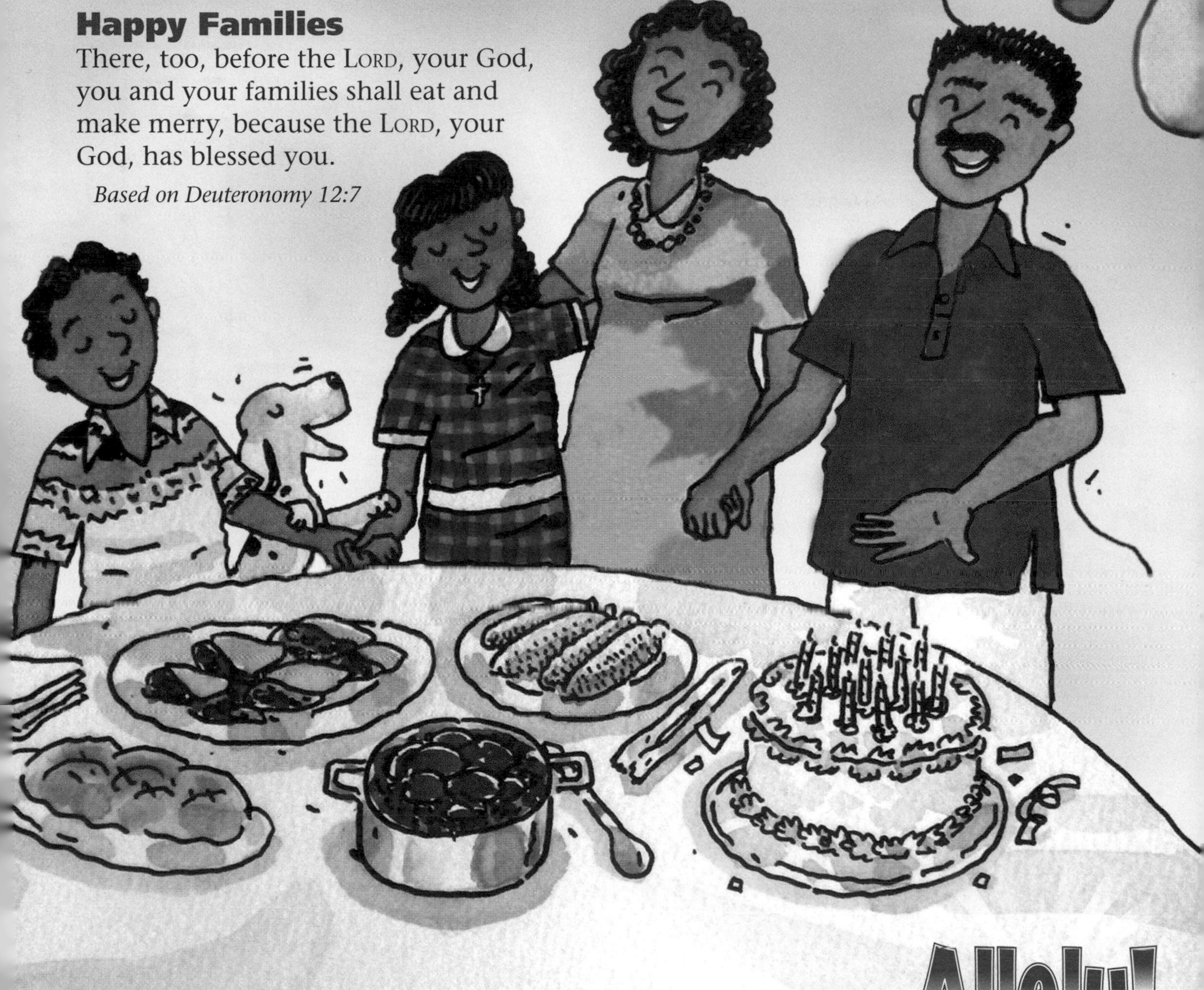

Lesson 13, Ages 4-5

Sharing Faith at Home Your child will be familiar with these Scripture words from class prayer. After reading this aloud, encourage the child to name ways your family has been blessed.

Through the Week

Discuss why it is important to gather with the Church community to celebrate Mass.

Ask Me!

Ask your child these questions, and see if he or she can give you the answers. *(If not, give a hint, and review the questions again later.)*

1. What do families do on special occasions? *(They celebrate together.)*
2. Who is the family of God? *(the Church)*
3. What is the greatest "family celebration" of the Church? *(the Mass)*

Setting the

Whe
They

Draw a path to show v

Draw a pi
your family

Family Table

Are
oing?

e each family is going.

of a place
to together.

Mealtime Prayer

Dear Jesus,
we thank you for
our families and
we praise you
for the celebrations we share.
Please bless our families
and keep us safe.
Amen.

Pray this prayer as a family.

Saint of the Week

Sergius of Radonezh (1314–1392)

Feast Day: September 25

Did you know?

As a child, Sergius of Russia had difficulty learning to read. According to legend, an angel visited him and gave him the ability to read. Sergius helped many people lead prayerful lives.

Saint Sergius, pray for us!

Parent Notes

In this week's lesson your child learned

- Families celebrate special times together.
- The Church is the family of God.
- The Mass is the greatest "family celebration" of the Church.

It Helps to Know

The *Catechism* teaches us that

- through the Eucharistic meal, we as a Church draw closer to Christ and to one another. (*CCC,* 1396)
- the celebration of the Mass begins with the Sign of the Cross. This conveys that God is present, and the actions of the Mass will be performed in his name.
- at Mass we are united as one family—sons and daughters of God the Father. We gather as the Body of Christ. We are brought together by the Spirit, who has worked in our hearts to help us hear and respond to God's call.
- we experience Christ in the Liturgy of the Word and, most completely in the Liturgy of the Eucharist. We are then sent forth to love and serve.

Keep It Simple

- Be sure that as your child learns about Mass in faith formation, he or she has an opportunity to experience the Mass through your faithful attendance as a family.
- Purchase a child's picture missal, so your child can use the pictures to follow along with what is happening at Mass. As your child grows and is ready, practice the prayers at home, and be sure to help him or her recite them in the Mass itself.

How Four- and Five-Year-Olds Understand the Lesson, by Joseph White, Ph.D.

Most four- and five-year-olds see the Mass as an adult event. Still, they love to sing, and can learn to sing along in Mass, especially the parts that are repeated week after week. (They are only likely to do this, however, if their parents make an effort to sing as well!) They are also capable of learning some of the shorter prayers and spoken responses of the Mass. Children this age may wish they could participate in the Eucharistic procession. Be sure to remind them that they will join the family someday at the Eucharistic table.

Visit **Allelu.com** for weekly Scripture readings, reflections, and activities.

My Family Cares for Me

This Week's Scripture Story

tells us that Jesus had a mother named Mary and a foster father named Joseph.

Caring for Baby Jesus

When Jesus was a newborn baby, an angel appeared to Joseph in a dream. He told Joseph that the king in their land wanted to harm Jesus, because he was afraid Jesus would become king. The angel told Joseph to take Jesus and Mary to Egypt where they would be safe.

Joseph did as the angel told him, and in the night, he left with Jesus and Mary to go to Egypt, where they stayed.

After the king died, the angel appeared to Joseph again and told him to return home with Jesus and Mary. They did as the angel instructed, and made their home in the town of Nazareth.

Based on Matthew 2:13–23

Sharing Faith at Home Share the story with your child by talking about its meaning or reading it aloud at bedtime.
Discussion starter: Share how you lived as Jesus taught today.

Through the Week

Talk about your own family, and look at family photos together. Point out pictures that show your family celebrating together and helping each other.

Ask Me!

Ask your child these questions, and see if he or she can give you the answers. *(If not, give a hint, and review the questions again later.)*

1. Who gave us our family? *(God gave us our family.)*
2. Who is the "Holy Family"? *(Jesus, Mary, and Joseph)*
3. How is our family like the Holy Family?

Setting the

The Ho
My

Draw a line to conn
Family. Then **dra**
of your family pray

Family Table

Family,
mily

ach family to the Holy
r **paste** a picture
r working together.

Mealtime Prayer

Dear Jesus,
you know how important
it is for children to be loved
and cared for in a family.
Thank you for our family.
Teach us to be
patient and kind
as we care for each other.
Amen.

Pray this prayer as a family.

Saint of the Week

The Virgin Mary
(first century)
Major Feast Days: January 1, August 15, December 8

Did you know?

Mary accepted God's will for her to become the Mother of God. Now we all can call her our heavenly mother.

Holy Mary,
Mother of God,
pray for us!

Parent Notes

In this week's lesson your child learned

- That God gives us a family to love and take care of us.
- That Jesus had a family, too: Mary, his mother, and Joseph, his foster father.

It Helps to Know

The *Catechism* teaches us that

- the home is "the first school of Christian life" (*CCC,* 1657), meaning that by God's design, families are the first and primary place children learn about God.
- children learn what they see and experience. That's why it is so important for parents to have a relationship with God. We can do this by spending some time reading the Scriptures, in prayer, and showing an attitude of thanksgiving to God in all that we do.
- through the Fourth Commandment, God has willed that, after him, we should honor our parents and those whom he has vested with authority for our good. (*CCC,* 2248)

Keep It Simple

- Show children the "holiness" of everyday family life. When you help your child with something, like tying a shoelace or opening a wrapper, tell him or her that God wants us to help each other.
- When you comfort your child when he or she is afraid, say, "When you can't see me, know that God is with you."
- When your child learns something new, tell him or her, "It makes God so happy to see you growing and learning new things, just like he planned."

How Four- and Five-Year-Olds Understand the Lesson, by Joseph White, Ph.D.

Four- and five-year-olds understand family as they experience it. For some, family includes their parent or parents and siblings, while for others, it includes extended family, especially in families in which other relatives live in the home. Parents can help children understand that families come in many different forms, but one very important purpose of families is to take care of children and help them grow to be the people God made them to be.

Visit **Allelu.com** for weekly Scripture readings, reflections, and activities.

We Live as Jesus Taught

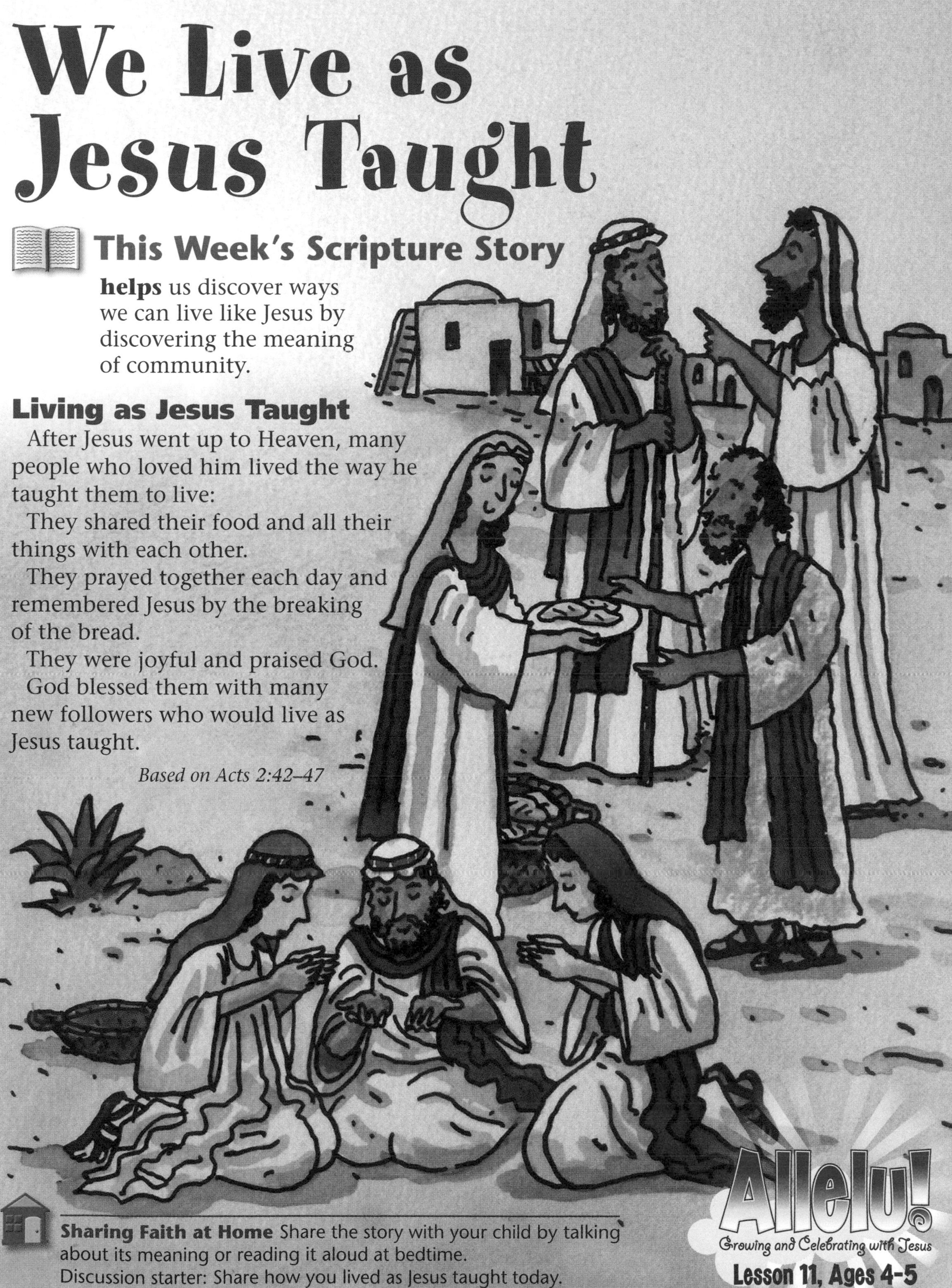

This Week's Scripture Story

helps us discover ways we can live like Jesus by discovering the meaning of community.

Living as Jesus Taught

After Jesus went up to Heaven, many people who loved him lived the way he taught them to live:

They shared their food and all their things with each other.

They prayed together each day and remembered Jesus by the breaking of the bread.

They were joyful and praised God.

God blessed them with many new followers who would live as Jesus taught.

Based on Acts 2:42–47

Sharing Faith at Home Share the story with your child by talking about its meaning or reading it aloud at bedtime.
Discussion starter: Share how you lived as Jesus taught today.

Through the Week

Have each member of the family pray for a friend.

Ask Me!

Ask your child these questions, and see if he or she can give you the answers. *(If not, give a hint, and review the questions again later.)*

1. What do we call a group of families and friends who do things together? *(a community)*
2. What are some of the communities to which we belong? *(school, neighborhood, parish church)*
3. What are some rules that we follow to get along with one another? *(Share, take turns, talk about problems instead of fighting.)*

Setting the

W
Being

Circle the childrer
Then **draw** a pictu

Family Table

Is … riend?

… are being friends.
… one of your friends.

Mealtime Prayer

Dear Jesus,
our loving friend and
our Savior, you ask us
to share with one another.
You ask us to pray together.
You ask us to love one another.
Please help us as
we try to share, pray,
and love this week.
Amen.

Pray this prayer as a family.

Saint of the Week

Margaret of Scotland (1045–1093)

Feast Day: November 16

Did you know?

Margaret of Scotland was a beloved queen whose faith, compassion, and leadership enabled her to bring a vibrant Catholic life to Scotland. **Saint Margaret, pray for us!**

Parent Notes

In this week's lesson your child learned

- A community is a group of families and friends who do things together. Our parish church is one of the communities to which we belong.
- All communities have rules about how members are to behave and treat one another.

It Helps to Know

Scripture tells us that

- we are called to live a life in communion with God and with one another.
- the early Church placed a high priority on living in community, with the early Christians living "together" and having "all things in common" (Acts 2:44).
- the cohesiveness of their community helped the early Christians "go into the whole world and proclaim the gospel to every creature" (Mark 16:15).

The *Catechism* teaches us that

- because humans are social by nature, the good of each individual is related to the common good. (*CCC,* 1905)

Keep It Simple

- Have regular family meals in which everyone gathers at the table, away from television and other distractions.
- Develop family rituals, especially around special occasions, but also around everyday events, such as bedtimes and mealtimes.

How Four- and Five-Year-Olds Understand the Lesson, by Joseph White, Ph.D.

The first "community" to which a child belongs is the family. It is here that the child first learns to be in relationship with others and the concept of community rules. For most four- and five-year-olds the parish church, religion class, or Catholic preschool will be their first experiences of the larger Christian community, and an early experience of the expectations that we share in a community of peers. The primary tasks for your child at this age include learning to share and take turns, to be patient, and to interact with others through play.

Visit **Allelu.com** for weekly Scripture readings, reflections, and activities.

Jesus Is Our King

This Week's Scripture

helps us praise Jesus who is God's Son and also King of Heaven and earth.

Sing Praise to the Lord

Shout with joy to the Lord, all
the earth.
Sing praise to the Lord with
the harp,
With trumpets shout with joy to the King!
Let the sea and what fills it resound,
Let the rivers clap their hands,
And the mountains shout with them
for joy,
Before the Lord who comes to rule
the earth!

Based on Psalm 98

Sharing Faith at Home Share the Scripture with your child by talking about its meaning or reading it aloud at bedtime. Discussion starter: Why is Jesus the most important king of all?

Through the Week

As a sign of respect for Jesus in the Eucharist, we genuflect before the Blessed Sacrament in the tabernacle whenever we enter or leave church. Practice genuflecting on your right knee.

Ask Me!

Ask your child these questions, and see if he or she can give you the answers. *(If not, give a hint, and review the questions again later.)*

1. Who is King of Heaven and earth? *(Jesus Christ)*
2. On what day do we celebrate the "kingship" of Jesus? *(the Feast of Christ the King)*
3. What is one way you can give praise to Jesus as King?

Setting the

Christ

Connect the dots t

Trace the letters to

2

4

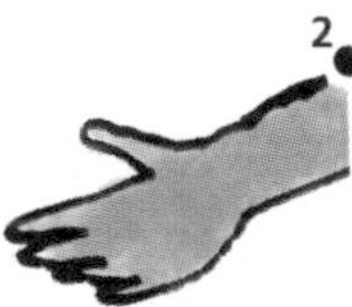

3

5

Christ

Family Table
e King
w a picture of Jesus.
who is in the picture.
9
7
8
6
ne King
Mealtime Prayer
Lord Jesus,
we come before you
as our King.
We worship and we praise you.
We thank you for your love
for us and the bounty
you share with us.
Hear our prayers always.
Amen.
Pray this prayer as a family.
Saint of the Week
David I of Scotland
(1080–1153)
Feast Day: May 24
Did you know?
Son of Saint Margaret of
Scotland and King Malcolm,
David I continued his
parents' work of serving the
poor, building schools and
hospitals, and strengthening
the Church in Scotland.
Saint David,
pray for us!

Parent Notes

In this week's lesson your child learned

- Jesus is the King of Heaven and the earth.
- We celebrate the "kingship" of Jesus on the feast of Christ the King.

It Helps to Know

The *Catechism* teaches us that

- Jesus Christ is the one whom the Father anointed with the Holy Spirit and established as Priest, Prophet, and King. (*CCC,* 783)
- Jesus "exercises his kingship by drawing all men to himself through his death and Resurrection" (*CCC,* 786). He will return at the end of time to judge the living and the dead. (CCC, 682)

Scripture tells us that

- Christ Jesus is the center of the four Gospels, the central part of Sacred Scripture. In Scripture, Jesus calls us to share in an unusual kind of "kingship." He says he came "not to be served, but to serve" (Mark 10:45).
- even though Jesus was God, "he did not deem equality with God, but, instead, he took the form of a slave" (Philippians 2:6–7), and because of this humility, God the Father exalted Jesus to the highest place.

Keep It Simple

- Children of this age tend to be very concrete in their thinking, so be sure images of Christ in your home include depictions of his royalty (e.g., an image of Christ as King) and his compassion and approachability (e.g., Jesus as the Good Shepherd).
- Have your child describe some qualities of a king, and discuss how those qualities do or do not apply to Jesus.

How Four- and Five-Year-Olds Understand the Lesson, by Joseph White, Ph.D.

Four- and five-year-olds are familiar with fairy tales and other stories about kings and queens, some of whom are good and approachable and some who are harsh or unkind. As your child gets to know Jesus both as friend and as king, the nature of Jesus, both human and divine, will become clearer.

Visit **Allelu.com** for weekly Scripture readings, reflections, and activities.

Jesus Is the Good Shepherd

This Week's Scripture Story

teaches us that Jesus called himself the "Good Shepherd" to help us understand how God cares for each of us.

The Good Shepherd

Jesus said, "I am the Good Shepherd. If a wolf comes to attack the sheep, a worker who is not a shepherd will run and hide, but a shepherd will give up his life to protect his sheep. I know my sheep and they know me, and I will lay down my life for my sheep."

Based on John 10:11–16

Sharing Faith at Home Enrich your child's understanding of the Scripture by talking about it at mealtime or at bedtime. Discussion starter: Why is Jesus called the Good Shepherd?

Through the Week

Talk about the ways God is a "Shepherd" to us by giving us the things we need, protecting and comforting us, and giving us rules so we can be safe and do our best.

Ask Me!

Ask your child these questions, and see if he or she can give you the answers. *(If not, give a hint, and review the questions again later.)*

1. Who called himself the Good Shepherd? *(Jesus)*

2. Who are his sheep? *(We are.)*

3. How is Jesus like a good shepherd? *(He takes care of us like a shepherd takes care of his sheep.)*

Setting the

Kn
the

Find and **color** t
that are the same.
the Good Shepherd

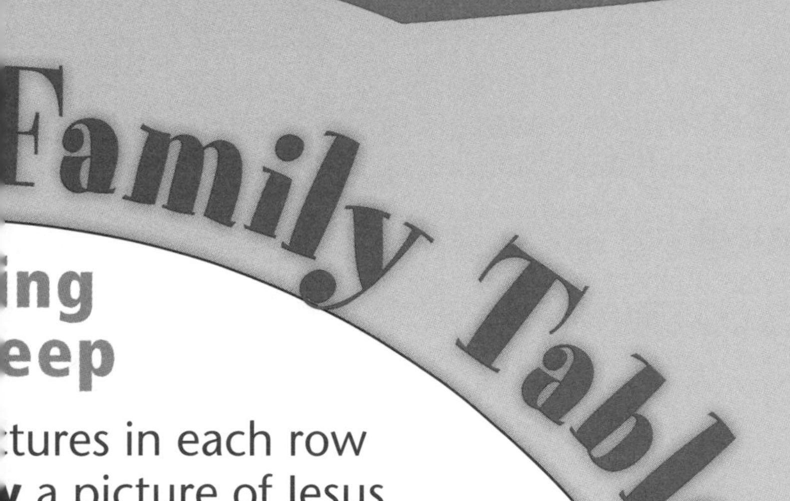

ing
eep

tures in each row
v a picture of Jesus
g care of the sheep.

Mealtime Prayer

The Lord is
my shepherd,
there is nothing I will want.
Only goodness and love
will follow me
all the days of my life.
I will dwell
in the house of the Lord
for years to come.

Based on Psalm 23

Pray this prayer as a family.

Saint of the Week

Cuthbert **(c. 643–687)**
Feast Day: March 20

Did you know?

Saint Cuthbert was a shepherd who later became a monk. He lived a holy life, and was known for his generosity and his gift of healing. He became known as the "Wonder Worker of Britain."

Saint Cuthbert, pray for us!

Parent Notes

In this week's lesson your child learned

- Jesus called himself the Good Shepherd.
- Jesus takes care of us like a good shepherd takes care of his sheep.

It Helps to Know

Scripture tells us that

- Jesus' comparison of himself with a good shepherd in this lesson reminds us of Psalm 23, which begins, "The Lord is my shepherd, I shall not want" (Psalm 23:1). The psalmist describes a shepherd who gives his sheep everything they need—food and drink, goodness and mercy, courage and safety.

The *Catechism* teaches us that

- a loving parent nurtures a child and sets limits for him or her. God the Father shepherds us with nurture as well as limits, which come in the form of his commandments and the guidance of the Church. (*CCC,* 2062–2063)
- the Pope is the shepherd of the Church on earth. (*CCC,* 880–882, 936–937)

Keep It Simple

- Pray Psalm 23 together as a family, and act out parts of the psalm using props such as sheep figurines from a farm toy set or sheep made from cotton balls and paper.
- Talk about how parents help Jesus be the Good Shepherd to their children by caring for them and providing for what they need.

How Four- and Five-Year-Olds Understand the Lesson, by Joseph White, Ph.D.

Most four- and five-year-olds are interested in animals and curious about those who care for them. This makes the story of the Good Shepherd especially engaging for children this age. Although analogies are difficult for them, because they think in concrete terms, children this age can learn that just as a shepherd gives the sheep the things they need to live, God gives us what we need. Just as the shepherd protects the sheep, God protects us. Of course, in your child's life, you are the most powerful example of the Good Shepherd, shown through your loving nurture and the limits and guidance you provide.

Jesus Cares for Our Needs

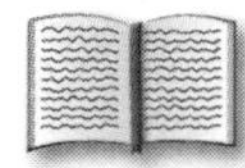

This Week's Scripture Story

helps us understand that God provides for all our needs.

Jesus Feeds Many People

A large crowd had gathered to listen to Jesus teach. Now it was late in the day, and Jesus wanted to give the people food to eat. His disciples wondered how that would be possible.

One of the disciples said to Jesus, "There is a boy here who has five loaves and two fish, but how will that help us feed so many people?" Jesus said to the disciples, "Have the people sit." Then he took the loaves and fish, gave thanks to God, and told the disciples to give them to the people.

Even though there were almost five thousand people there, everyone had enough to eat.

Based on Luke 9:12–17 and John 6:1–11

Sharing Faith at Home Share the Scripture story with your child by reading it aloud as a family at mealtime.
Discussion starter: What would you say to Jesus if you were there?

Through the Week

Discuss simple ways your family can participate in God's work of caring for others, such as by being kind and by sharing.

Ask Me!

Ask your child these questions, and see if he or she can give you the answers. *(If not, give a hint, and review the questions again later.)*

1. What did the child in this week's story share? *(five loaves of bread and two fish)*
2. How many people did the loaves and fish feed? *(5,000, or "thousands")*
3. Why did Jesus give food to all the people? *(because he cared about them)*

Setting the

Loaves

Find and **draw a c**
bread and each f

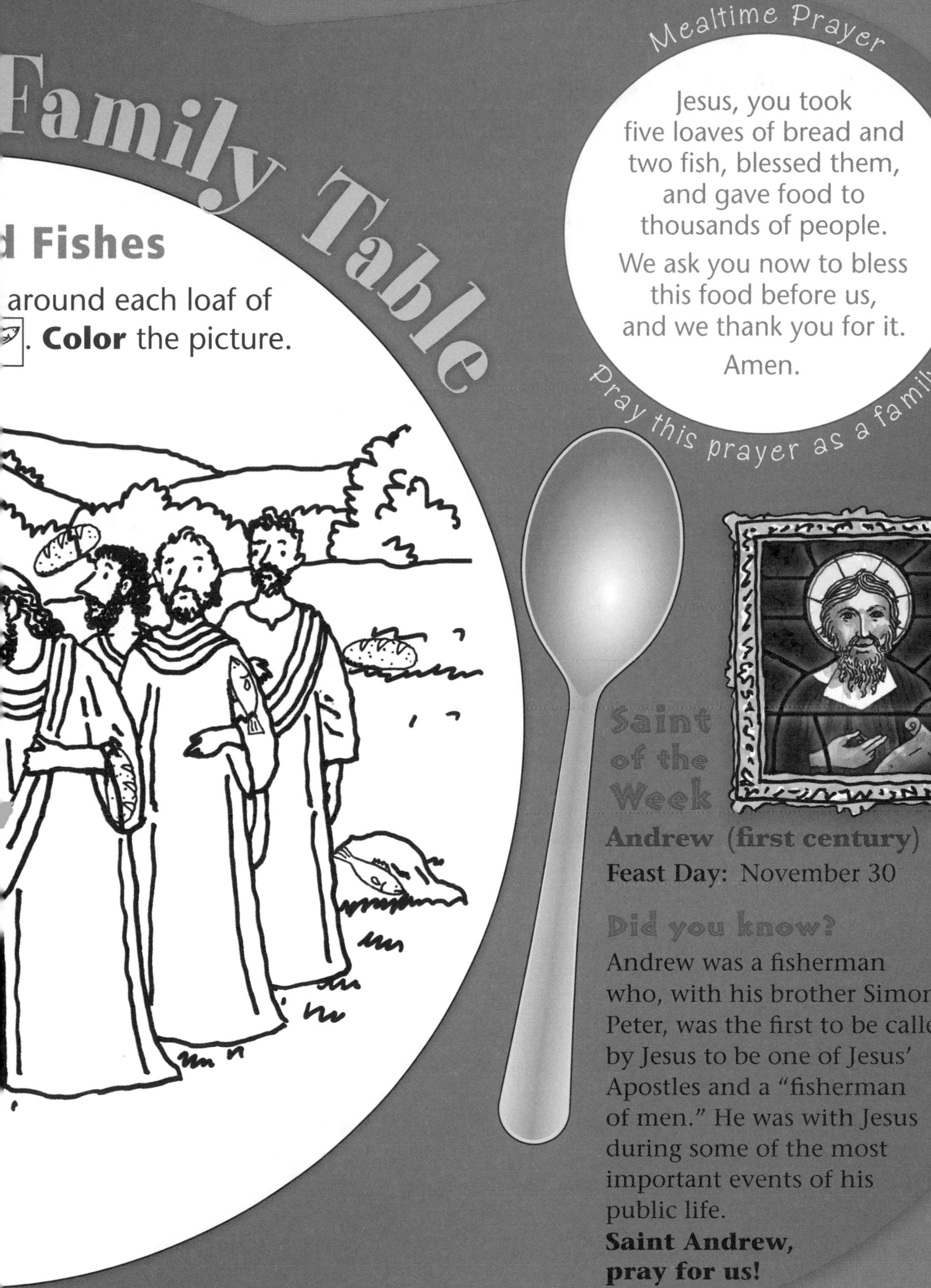

Family Table

d Fishes

around each loaf of . **Color** the picture.

Mealtime Prayer

Jesus, you took
five loaves of bread and
two fish, blessed them,
and gave food to
thousands of people.
We ask you now to bless
this food before us,
and we thank you for it.
Amen.

Pray this prayer as a family.

Saint of the Week

Andrew (first century)

Feast Day: November 30

Did you know?

Andrew was a fisherman who, with his brother Simon Peter, was the first to be called by Jesus to be one of Jesus' Apostles and a "fisherman of men." He was with Jesus during some of the most important events of his public life.

Saint Andrew, pray for us!

Parent Notes

In this week's lesson your child learned

- Jesus made sure the crowd of people listening to him did not go hungry.
- God wants us to work together to give others what they need.

It Helps to Know

Scripture tells us that

- we can do all things through Jesus, who strengthens us (Philippians 4:13). If we ask God to help us be the examples and teachers he calls us to be, he will support us in this role.

The *Catechism* teaches us that

- the Catholic Church places a high priority on the role of parents in the process of Christian formation. The family is the "primary agent of an incarnate transmission of the faith" (*CCC,* 207). Parents are the first and most important teachers of their children, especially when it comes to things of God. It is the family that shows, through relationships and actions, how Christian principles inform the decisions and actions of daily life.

Keep It Simple

- Clarify the wonder of what Jesus did when he multiplied the loaves and fish by taking a few pieces of bread at the family table and asking your child, "Can we turn a little bit of bread into enough to feed a huge crowd?" When your child agrees that this is impossible for an ordinary human being, remind him or her that God did do it on that special day, because God can do anything.
- Discuss ways you can help others by sharing your family's blessings with others who are in need.

How Four- and Five-Year-Olds Understand the Lesson, by Joseph White, Ph.D.

The story of Jesus' feeding of the 5,000 is quite intriguing for young children. It's an amazing feat, to be sure, and can seem like a "magic trick" in the mind of a child. But this was no trick. God, who created matter out of nothing, can change (or multiply) matter in ways we do not understand. Stories of Jesus' miracles are wonderful ways to teach young children the awesome power of God, and the amazing things God is able to do through us if we cooperate with him.

Visit **Allelu.com** for weekly Scripture readings, reflections, and activities.

Jesus Is God's Son

This Week's Scripture Story

helps us understand Jesus Christ as the Son of God and the Second Person of the Holy Trinity.

The Baptism of Jesus

Jesus went to the river. There, his cousin John was baptizing people.

Jesus asked John to baptize him. When John baptized Jesus, God the Holy Spirit came to Jesus, like a beautiful dove. Everyone heard the voice of God the Father, who said, "This is by beloved Son."

Based on Matthew 3:13–17

Sharing Faith at Home Share the story of Jesus' baptism with your child by talking about the story or reading it aloud at bedtime. Discussion starter: Tell a story about your child's day of baptism.

Through the Week

At the beginning or end of each day, bless one another by making the Sign of the Cross on each other's foreheads.

Ask Me!

Ask your child these questions, and see if he or she can give you the answers. *(If not, give a hint, and review the questions again later.)*

1. What did you learn about God this week? *(that there are Three Persons in one God.)*
2. What are the names of the Three Divine Persons in one God? *(God the Father, God the Son, and God the Holy Spirit)*
3. Which of the Three Divine Persons is Jesus? *(God the Son)*

Setting the

Finish t

Follow the pattern
in each row. **Talk** ab
of t

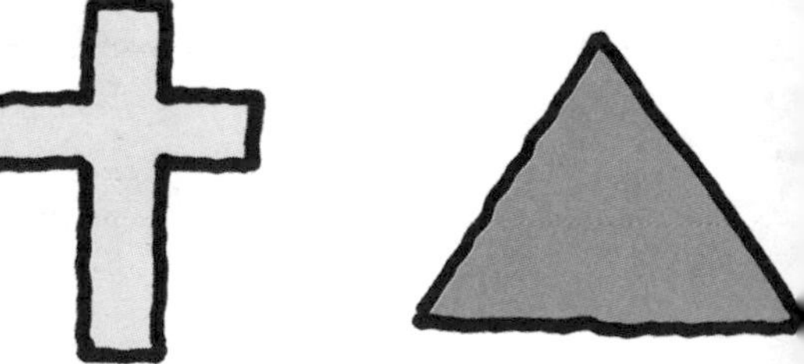

Family Table
Pattern
w what comes next
ach of these symbols
ity.
Mealtime Prayer
In the Name
of the Father,
and of the Son,
and of the Holy Spirit.
You are one God,
in Father, Son, and Holy Spirit.
Thank you for
loving us always.
Amen.
Pray this prayer as a family.
Saint of the Week
Patrick of Ireland
(389–461)
Feast Day: March 17
Did you know?
Patrick, who as a young
English boy was taken to
Ireland to work, is credited
with bringing Christianity to
the Irish people.
Saint Patrick,
pray for us!

Parent Notes

In this week's lesson your child learned

- The Holy Trinity is one God.
- There is one God in Three Divine Persons, called "God the Father, God the Son, and God the Holy Spirit."

It Helps to Know

Scripture tells us that

- although it is beyond our human understanding, God the Father, Son, and Holy Spirit are Three Divine Persons and yet mysteriously one.

The *Catechism* teaches us that

- through the Second Commandment, we must respect the Lord's name, which is holy. (*CCC,* 2161)
- in our Creed each Sunday, we proclaim that "We believe in one God, the Father... the Son... and the Holy Spirit." The *Catechism* calls the Holy Trinity "the central mystery of Christian faith and life" (*CCC,* 261).
- the family is created to be an image of the Trinity (*CCC,* 2205), and as such, can help us understand who God is.

Keep It Simple

- Teach your child the Sign of the Cross, a physical prayer in which we name God as Father, Son, and Holy Spirit.
- While it is sometimes difficult to find iconic representations of God the Father, it is fairly easy to find depictions of Jesus and the Holy Spirit in pictures, statues, and other icons. Place some of these visible symbols of God in your home, and talk about them occasionally, asking your child questions such as "Who is in this picture?" and "Name the Three Persons of God."

How Four- and Five-Year-Olds Understand the Lesson, by Joseph White, Ph.D.

The concept of a God who is one, but also three is difficult for young children to comprehend, even more so than for adults. Even so, the Trinity is such an important concept in our faith that we introduce it early in religious education, recognizing that the child's understanding of the Trinity should grow throughout his or her lifetime. Teaching about the Persons of the Trinity by name and sharing Scripture stories that show them in action sets a foundation that will help the child discover the nature of God and grow ever closer to him.

Visit **Allelu.com** for weekly Scripture readings, reflections, and activities.

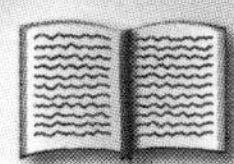

This Week's Scripture Story

helps us learn about the presentation of Baby Jesus at the Temple.

Simeon and Anna Meet Baby Jesus

Eight days after Jesus was born, Mary and Joseph took him to the Temple in Jerusalem to be blessed. An old man named Simeon and an old woman named Anna were there, too, that day. Both were holy people who loved God greatly and prayed often. They knew that God had promised that someday he would send a savior into the world, called a Messiah. When they saw this baby, they knew he was the Messiah. Simeon held Baby Jesus and thanked God for this most wonderful gift. Anna, too, thanked God, and told others that God had kept his promise.

Based on Luke 2:22–38

Sharing Faith at Home Share the story with your child by talking about its meaning or reading it aloud at bedtime.
Discussion starter: Say a prayer thanking God for sending us Jesus.

Through the Week

Talk about ways you see Jesus in the people you meet each day.

Ask Me!

Ask your child these questions, and see if he or she can give you the answers. *(If not, give a hint, and review the questions again later.)*

1. Where did Mary and Joseph take Baby Jesus? *(to the Temple)*
2. Whom did Jesus, Mary, and Joseph meet at the Temple? *(two holy people named Simeon and Anna)*
3. How did Simeon and Anna feel about meeting the baby Jesus? *(They were happy. They thanked God.)*

Setting the

Me
Bab

Color the picture o
Temple. **Use** the code
to tell who Simeo

Baby

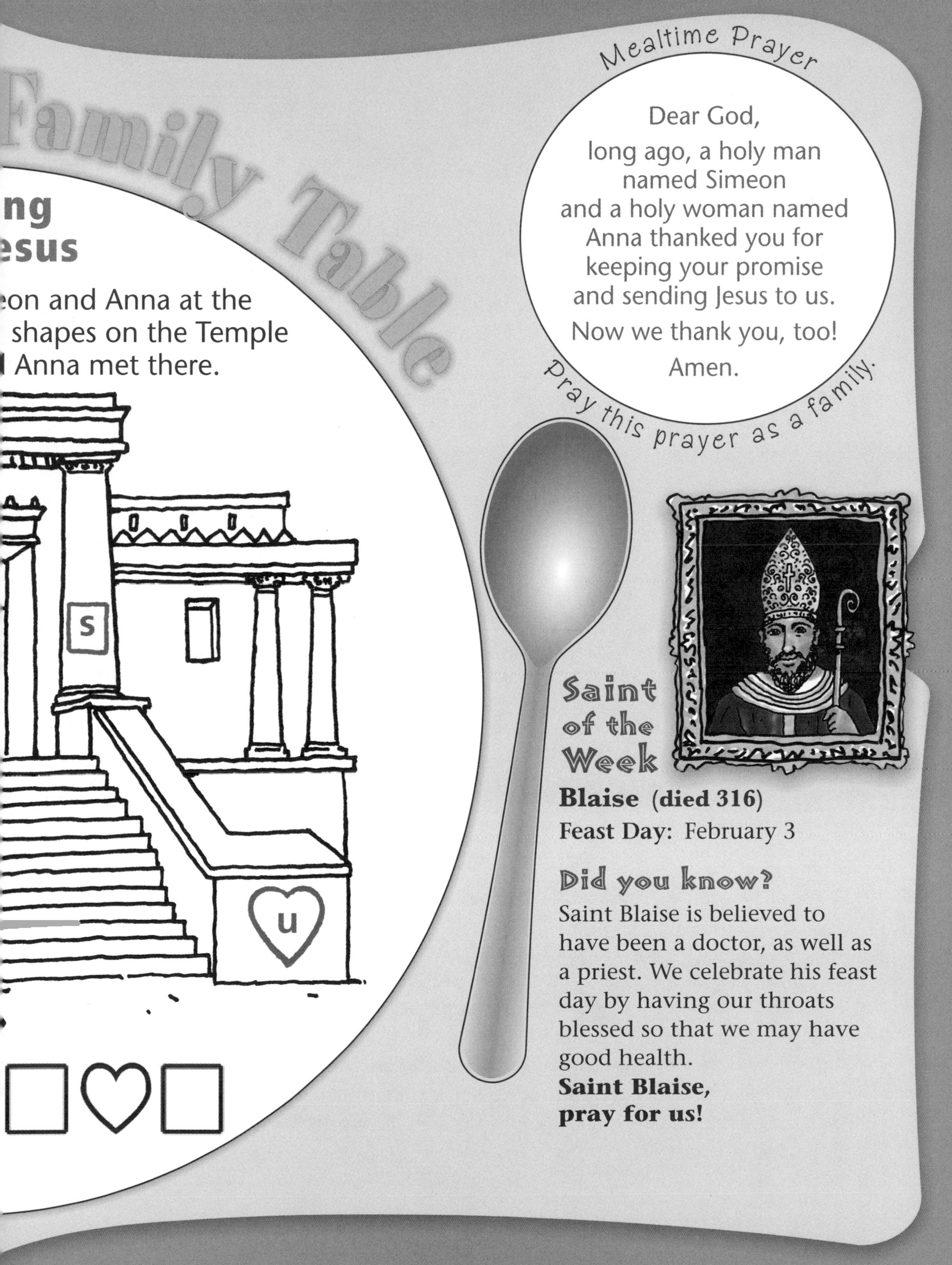

Family Table
ng
esus
eon and Anna at the
shapes on the Temple
Anna met there.
s
u
Mealtime Prayer
Dear God,
long ago, a holy man
named Simeon
and a holy woman named
Anna thanked you for
keeping your promise
and sending Jesus to us.
Now we thank you, too!
Amen.
Pray this prayer as a family.
Saint of the Week

Blaise **(died 316)**
Feast Day: February 3

Did you know?

Saint Blaise is believed to have been a doctor, as well as a priest. We celebrate his feast day by having our throats blessed so that we may have good health.

Saint Blaise, pray for us!

Parent Notes

In this week's lesson your child learned

- Mary and Joseph took Baby Jesus to the Temple, where two holy people named Simeon and Anna who recognized Jesus as the Messiah.
- God promised Simeon that he would see Jesus someday, and he met Jesus at the Temple.

It Helps to Know

Scripture tells us that

- when Simeon saw the Baby Jesus, he immediately knew he was the Messiah. Filled with the Holy Spirit, he prophesied that Jesus would be a light to the Gentiles and the glory of Israel. (See Luke 2:32–33.)

The *Catechism* teaches us that

- the parish is the Eucharistic community and the heart of the liturgical life of Christian families. (*CCC,* 2226)
- education in the faith by the parents should begin in the child's earliest years. Family catechesis precedes, accompanies, and enriches other forms of instruction in the faith. (*CCC,* 2226)

Keep It Simple

- Talk with your child about his or her baptism and compare it to Jesus' presentation in the Temple.
- Make the lessons of this week come alive by attending a parish event designed for all ages and by introducing your child to adults you know in the parish.

How Four- and Five-Year-Olds Understand the Lesson, by Joseph White, Ph.D.

Children who attend Mass with their families have some sense of what is taking place in the story of the presentation. They, too, have been brought to God's house by their parents and have met older members of the faith community. The element of prophecy in the story of the presentation is still very much a mystery to children this age, but they can comprehend that God promised Simeon he would see the Messiah before he died, and that Simeon did—just as God told him.

Visit **Allelu.com** for weekly Scripture readings, reflections, and activities.

We Thank You, God

This Week's Scripture Story

reminds us that we should give thanks and praise to God for all that he does for us.

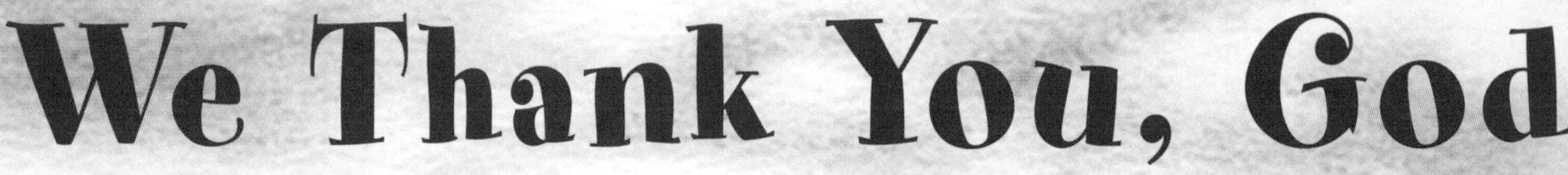

Giving Thanks to God

Jesus was on a journey to the city of Jerusalem. As he got close to a village along the way, a group of men who were very sick shouted, "Jesus, please help us!" Jesus said to the men, "Go and show yourselves to the priests." The men did as Jesus told them. As they walked away, they were healed. Jesus had cured them. One of them returned to Jesus and praised him for the miracle.

Jesus was disappointed that only one man gave him thanks. He blessed the man for his faith and sent him on his way.

Based on Luke 17:11–19

Sharing Faith at Home Help your child understand the Scripture story by acting it out together.
Discussion starter: Why is it important to say thank you to Jesus?

Through the Week

Make an extra effort to pray a grace or prayer before each meal in thanksgiving to God.

Ask Me!

Ask your child these questions, and see if he or she can give you the answers. *(If not, give a hint, and review the questions again later.)*

1. Who has done great things for us? *(God has done great things for us.)*
2. What are some of the things God does for us? *(He gives us food, a place to live, family, sent his only Son, Jesus.)*
3. What should we say to God for giving us these great things?" *(Thank you.)*

Setting the

W
Tha

All the people in the p
the pictures that show
Then **draw** on
thanks i

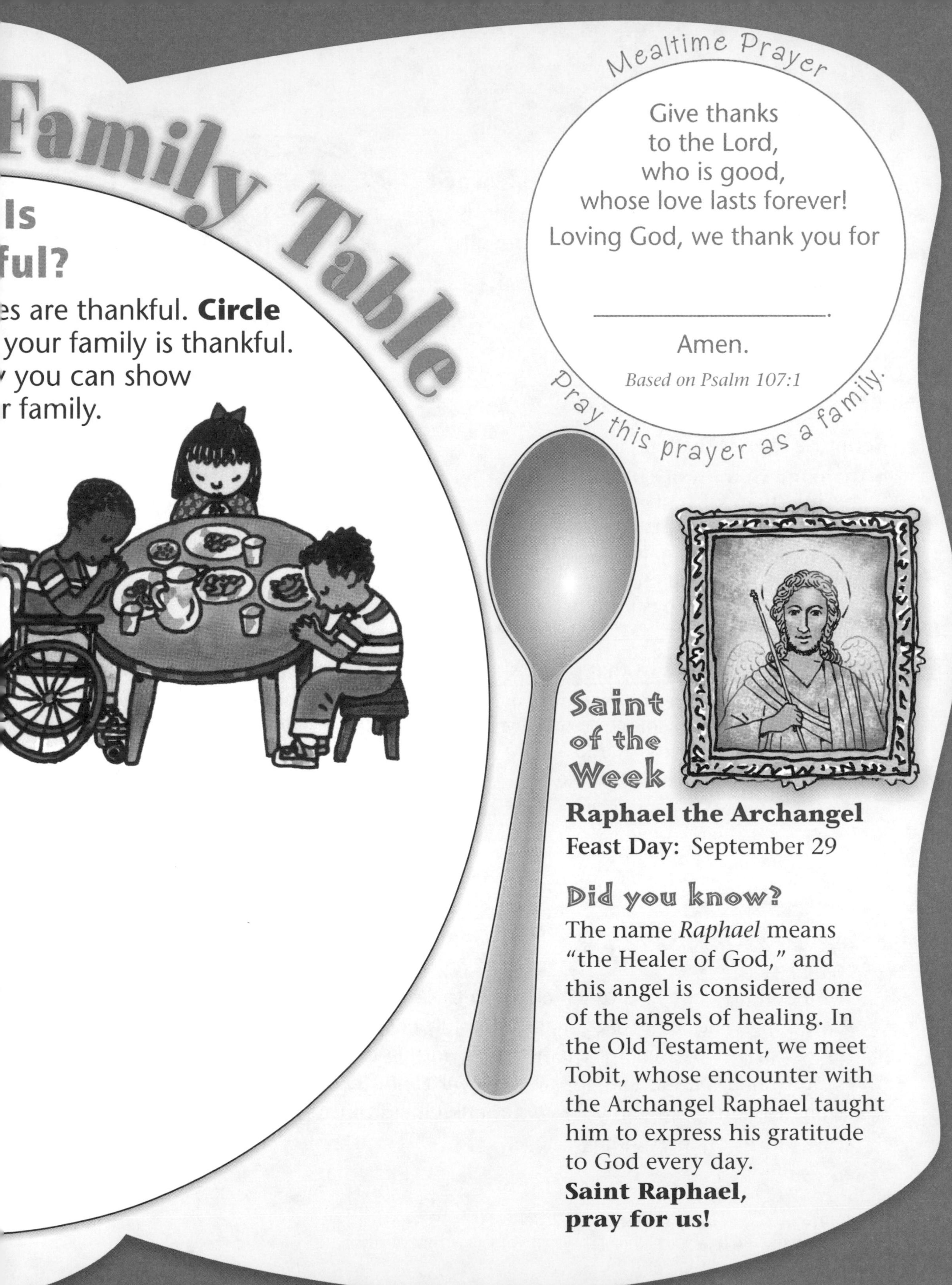

Family Table

Is
ful?

es are thankful. **Circle**
your family is thankful.
you can show
r family.

Mealtime Prayer

Give thanks
to the Lord,
who is good,
whose love lasts forever!
Loving God, we thank you for

_______________________.

Amen.

Based on Psalm 107:1

Pray this prayer as a family.

Saint of the Week

Raphael the Archangel

Feast Day: September 29

Did you know?

The name *Raphael* means "the Healer of God," and this angel is considered one of the angels of healing. In the Old Testament, we meet Tobit, whose encounter with the Archangel Raphael taught him to express his gratitude to God every day.

Saint Raphael,
pray for us!

Parent Notes

In this week's lesson your child learned

- God has done many good things for us.
- We should tell God "thank you" for all that he does.

It Helps to Know

Scripture tells us that

- thanking God for our blessings and sharing them with others should be a priority of every Christian family.
- God has done so much for us that even in the most difficult circumstances, we can always find things for which to be thankful.

The *Catechism* teaches us that

- we should make every prayer, and every need—every circumstance of our lives—an occasion for giving thanks. (*CCC,* 2638)

Keep It Simple

- As a family, take time – either in the car or at the dining table – to name blessings in your life. Talk about good things that have happened this week, material goods you are grateful for, people and experiences for which you are thankful, and so forth.
- Discuss various ways to show God you are grateful through responsible use of what you are given, prayers of thanksgiving, and sharing of what you have with others.

How Four- and Five-Year-Olds Understand the Lesson, by Joseph White, Ph.D.

From an early age, we teach children to say "thank you" when they are given something. The idea that an all-powerful, unseen God is the giver of good things is still abstract for them. God's work in the world is something they will come to understand and appreciate over time. By your giving to them without asking to be repaid and your own thankfulness to God, you will help them grow in this understanding.

Visit **Allelu.com** for weekly Scripture readings, reflections, and activities.

We Talk to God

This Week's Scripture Story

focuses on prayer as conversation with God.

Jesus Teaches Us to Pray

One day, one of Jesus' disciples said to him, "Lord, teach us to pray."

Jesus said, "This is how you should pray." He taught his disciples this prayer.

Our Father who art in heaven,
hallowed be thy name.
Thy kingdom come.
Thy will be done on earth as it is in heaven.
Give us this day our daily bread,
and forgive us our trespasses,
as we forgive those who trespass against us,
and lead us not into temptation,
but deliver us from evil.

Based on Matthew 6:9–13; Luke 11:1–4

Sharing Faith at Home Share the story with your child by talking about events in the story or reading it aloud at bedtime. Discussion starter: What prayers can we pray as a family?

Through the Week

If you don't have a prayer table in your home, create one, allowing each family member to help decorate this sacred space. Then plan and lead prayer time.

Ask Me!

Ask your child these questions, and see if he or she can give you the answers. *(If not, give a hint, and review the questions again later.)*

1. What is talking with God called? *(prayer)*
2. Why does God want us to talk with him? *(because he is our loving Father)*
3. Who teaches you how to pray?

Setting the

What's

In each row, **write** a
Write a 2 by what ha
by what happened t
your family the

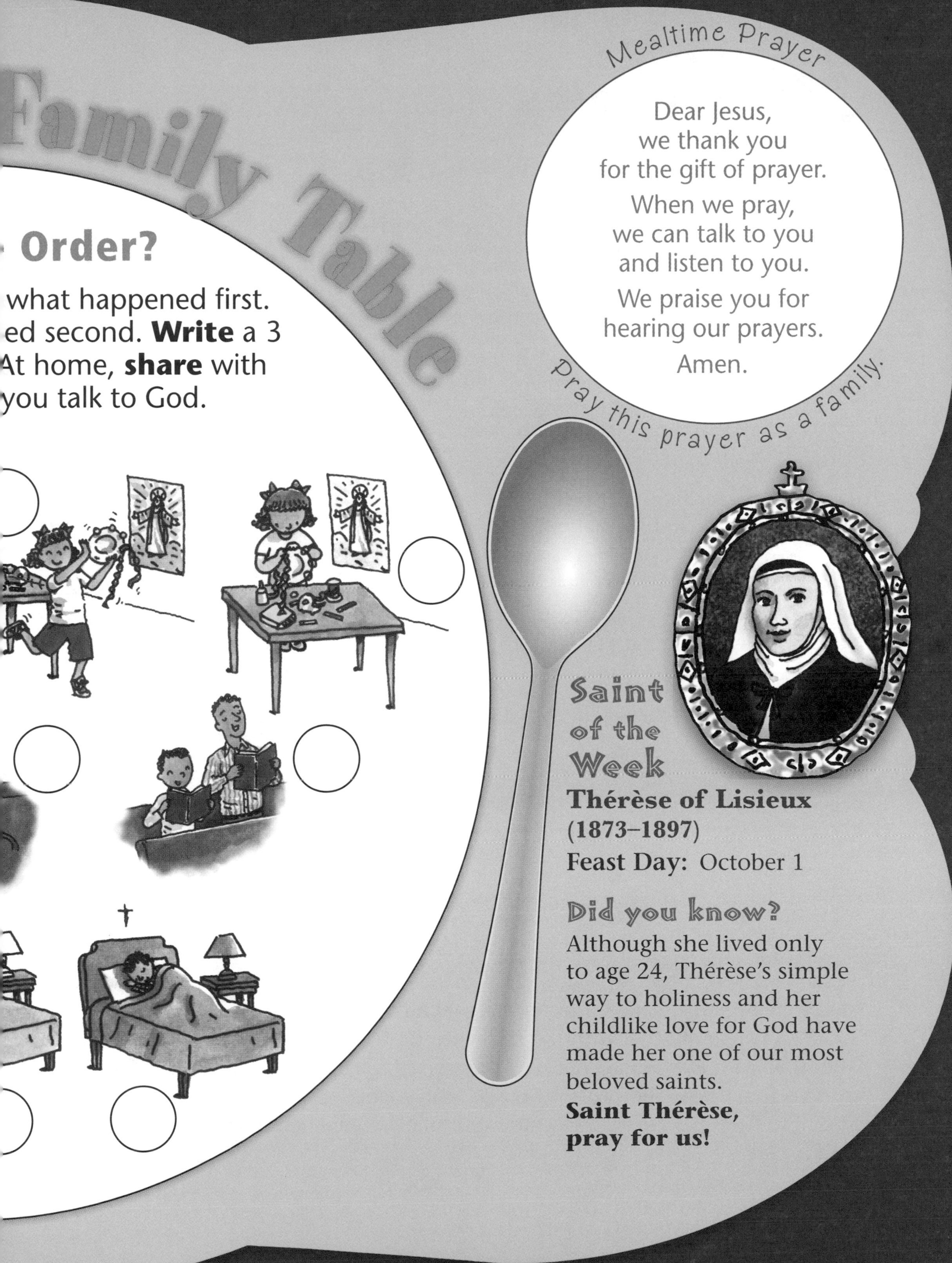
Family Table
Order?
what happened first.
ed second. **Write** a 3
At home, **share** with
you talk to God.
Mealtime Prayer
Dear Jesus,
we thank you
for the gift of prayer.
When we pray,
we can talk to you
and listen to you.
We praise you for
hearing our prayers.
Amen.
Pray this prayer as a family.
Saint of the Week
Thérèse of Lisieux
(1873–1897)
Feast Day: October 1
Did you know?
Although she lived only
to age 24, Thérèse's simple
way to holiness and her
childlike love for God have
made her one of our most
beloved saints.
Saint Thérèse,
pray for us!

Parent Notes

In this week's lesson your child learned

- God is our friend, and wants us to talk with him.
- There are many ways to pray.

It Helps to Know

Scripture tells us that

- children's trust in the unseen is perhaps what led Jesus to say, "Let the little children come to me, for the kingdom of heaven belongs to such as these" (Matthew 19:14).

The *Catechism* teaches us that prayer is conversation with God. We can pray using the five basic forms of prayer (*CCC*, 2625–2643):

- Praise: We recognize God for who he is.
- Blessing: We accept God's gifts and recognize him as their source. We exalt God for his greatness
- Thanksgiving: We extol God for what he has done for us.
- Petition: We ask God for the things we need.
- Intercession: We pray on another's behalf.

Keep It Simple

To build the foundation for your child's prayer life:

- Use a mixture of traditional and spontaneous prayer.
- Use the five forms of prayer when you pray.
- Make time for family prayer!

How Four- and Five-Year-Olds Understand the Lesson, by Joseph White, Ph.D.

It is a testament to the natural spiritual capacity of children that kids usually have no problem at all with the concept of a God who is invisible, but with them, as well as communicating with them through the natural world and the people they love. Therefore, this age is an excellent time to teach children to speak to God as a friend, as a father, as one who understands their language and is waiting to hear from them.

Visit **Allelu.com** for weekly Scripture readings, reflections, and activities.

God Made Me Special

This Week's Scripture Story

reminds us that we each are a special creation of God.

God Created All People

Long ago, God made the whole world. He made the sky, mountains and oceans, trees, stars, animals, and flowers. When God made people, he made them to be like him. Then he gave them all the plants and animals he created to take care of and to have for food. He said to them, "You are responsible for every living thing."

God looked at all that he had created and said, "This is good!"

Based on Genesis 1:26–31

Sharing Faith at Home Share the story with your child by talking about events in the story or reading it aloud at bedtime. Discussion starter: Name one way you care for God's creation.

Through the Week

Make an extra effort to pray a prayer of thanks to God before each meal.

Ask Me!

Ask your child these questions, and see if he or she can give you the answers. *(If not, give a hint, and review the questions again later.)*

1. Who made you? *(God made me.)*
2. How does God feel about all that he created? *(that it is good)*
3. How does God feel about you? *(God loves me. He is happy with what he made. I am very special to him.)*

Setting the

God C Beautiful

Circle the beaut
Draw or **paste** a
enjoying

Family Table
nted a
rld for Me
hings God made.
ure of your family
Creation.

Mealtime Prayer

Dear God,
our Creator,
we thank you for making us.
We praise you because you
made us to be like you.
We thank you that
we are wonderful!
Amen.

Pray this prayer as a family.

Saint of the Week

Joseph of Cupertino (1603–1663)

Feast Day: September 18

Did you know?

As a young man, Joseph of Cupertino was known for not being very clever. When he became a Franciscan, he grew in his love for God and became known for the many miracles God worked through him.

Saint Joseph, pray for us!

Parent Notes

In this week's lesson your child learned

- God made each of us and loves us.
- God is really happy with how he made us. We are very special to him.

It Helps to Know

Scripture tells us that

- after God created people, he looked upon his creation "and saw that it was very good" (Genesis 1:31).

The *Catechism* teaches us that

- although we might understand the biology of life, we cannot fully comprehend its mystery—how a new soul comes into being out of nothing. This is a mystery of the divine work of Creation. (*CCC,* 297)
- God created us to do good things, to show love to him and to others.
- Adam and Eve transmitted to all people their own first sin, known as Original Sin. We are therefore deprived of original holiness and justice. (*CCC,* 417)

Keep It Simple

- With your child, read the story of Creation in the Bible. Explain that God is the author of the Bible, which is the holy book of the Church.
- Make handprints using finger paints, clay, or some other medium that will show the small lines of the hands and fingers. Explain that each finger print is unique and special. Tell your child that in the same way, there is no one exactly like him or her.

How Four- and Five-Year-Olds Understand the Lesson, by Joseph White, Ph.D.

Most four- and five-year-olds know very little about how they came into being, and many have not even begun asking this question. It is possible, however, for them to learn that God made the world and everything in it, including people. Equally important is for children to begin to understand that God knows them personally, and that he is pleased with how he made them. He loves them just the way they are, and will help them become all that he made them to be.

Visit **Allelu.com** for weekly Scripture readings, reflections, and activities.

God Created the World

This Week's Scripture Story

reminds us that God created the universe and all its wonders, and that God blessed all Creation.

The Story of Creation

When God created the world, the earth was shapeless and dark, with a mighty wind sweeping over the land.

God said, "Let there be light." He saw how good the light was. Then he separated the light from the darkness and created day and night.

God created the sky. Then he collected all the water and created seas and oceans, and separated it from the dry land. On the dry land he created trees, grasses, and plants of every kind.

God said, "Let there be different lights in the sky—for day and for night." He made the two great lights, the sun for day and the moon for night. He set them in the sky.

God then said, "I will fill the earth with countless creatures." He created all the fish of the sea, the birds in the sky, and the animals on dry land.

God saw how good all his Creation was and blessed it.

Based on Genesis 1:1–22

Sharing Faith at Home Share the Scripture with your child by reading it aloud at bedtime and talking about its meaning. Discussion starter: What is your favorite image on this page? Why?

Through the Week

Pay attention to things in nature you sometimes take for granted, such as a beautiful flower, the color of a leaf, the falling rain, or a sunny sky.

Ask Me!

Ask your child these questions, and see if he or she can give you the answers. *(If not, give a hint, and review the questions again later.)*

1. Who made everything in nature? *(God did.)*
2. What are the four seasons God made? *(spring, summer, fall, and winter)*
3. What is one thing you especially love in God's Creation?

Setting the

Thankf

Draw a blue circle ar
for in winter. **Draw** a g
can thank God for in the
picture of how you can

Family Table

n
All Year

what you are thankful
circle around what you
ng. In the center, **draw** a
k God in prayer all year.

Mealtime Prayer

Blessed are you,
God of all Creation,
for giving us the gifts of
spring, summer, autumn,
and winter!
Amen.

Pray this prayer as a family.

Saint of the Week

Columba of Iona (521–597)

Feast Day: June 9

Did you know?

Saint Columba is known as one of the "Twelve Apostles of Ireland." He founded many monasteries in Ireland, an achievement that strengthened Christianity in Western Europe after the fall of the Roman Empire in the West.

Saint Columba, pray for us!

Parent Notes

In this week's lesson your child learned

- God made everything in nature.
- God made the seasons: spring, summer, fall, and winter.

It Helps to Know

Scripture tells us that

- God created all the universe and all living things, and gave it to us to enjoy and care for. (See Genesis 1:26–30.)

The *Catechism* teaches us that

- God made the world and everything in it (*CCC,* 198). The beauty of God's Creation calls us to respect the Creator and follow his will.
- by examining God's Creation, we discover the laws of nature (*CCC,* 341), which we are able to apply to our own lives.

Keep It Simple

- Talk about the changing of the seasons and about how seasons are part of God's wonderful Creation.
- Spend time in seasonal activities, such as finding colorful leaves in fall, planting flowers in spring, and so forth.

How Four- and Five-Year-Olds Understand the Lesson, by Joseph White, Ph.D.

Four- and five-year-olds often understand how the weather and natural surroundings change with the seasons, particularly if they live in a climate that has pronounced seasonal changes. They become excited about finding colorful leaves, playing in snow, and swimming or playing in water when it's hot outside. Children who live in climates with less pronounced seasonal changes may still understand the seasons from books and videos, as well as the holidays they celebrate at various times of the year.

Visit **Allelu.com** for weekly Scripture readings, reflections, and activities.

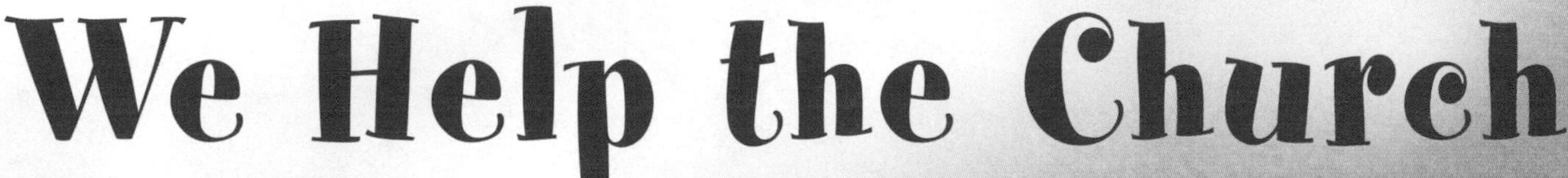

We Help the Church

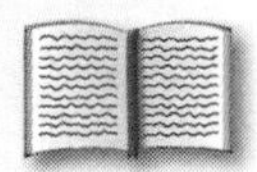

This Week's Scripture

focuses on all the people who help fulfill the Church's mission by using their talents in various ways.

Our Gifts

My friends,

The Holy Spirit gives each person gifts to do God's work in the world. Some people's gifts help them talk about Jesus, others' gifts help them heal sick people, and others have gifts that help them teach. There are many other gifts, and the Holy Spirit gives them to us so we can help one other.

My love be with you all in Christ Jesus,

Paul

Based on 1 Corinthians 12:1, 4–11; 16:21, 24

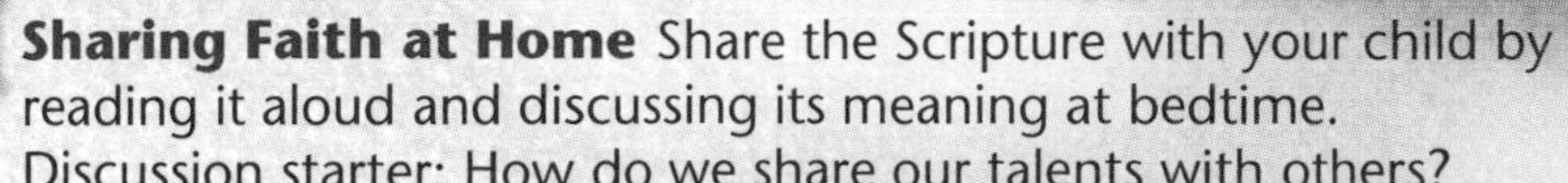

Sharing Faith at Home Share the Scripture with your child by reading it aloud and discussing its meaning at bedtime. Discussion starter: How do we share our talents with others?

Through the Week

Select one thing you can do as a family to help a neighbor or someone else.

Ask Me!

Ask your child these questions, and see if he or she can give you the answers. *(If not, give a hint, and review the questions again later.)*

1. What is a talent? *(a gift, something we do well)*
2. Who gives us talents? *(God)*
3. Why does God give us talents? *(to serve him and to help others)*

Setting the

Ou
Spec

Match the pictures to
using their gifts. **T**
a special gi

Family Table
wn
Gifts
v how the children are
bout how you use
d gave you.
Mealtime Prayer
Holy Spirit,
giver of gifts,
thank you for
our many talents.
Help us see how
we can use our gifts
to help each other
and to help
our church family.
Amen.
Pray this prayer as a family.
Saint of the Week
John Bosco (1815–1888)
Feast Day: January 31
Did you know?
John Bosco used his
tremendous energy and
talents to help countless
children live better lives and
come to know God.
Saint John Bosco,
pray for us!

Parent Notes

In this week's lesson your child learned

- God gives us talents, and calls us to use those talents for him.
- People in the Church help in many different ways.

It Helps to Know

Scripture tells us that

- we are all part of the one "Body of Christ," and must work together for the good of all.

The *Catechism* teaches us that

- God gives each of us different talents and calls us to share them with one another, both in the parish church and in the larger community. (*CCC,* 1937)

There are many ways to serve in our parish communities. Some people serve in the Mass as ushers, lectors, music ministers, altar servers, or extraordinary ministers of Holy Communion. Others serve through works of social service or charity, such as by helping with food pantries or outreach to the sick or homebound.

Keep It Simple

- One important precursor to service in the Church is service in the family, the "domestic church." As your child grows, be sure to provide ways he or she can help with household tasks.
- Look for opportunities to volunteer as a family in your parish, such as by helping with a parish mission project.

How Four- and Five-Year-Olds Understand the Lesson, by Joseph White, Ph.D.

Four- and five-year-olds are often aware of the various people working in different roles in their Parish Church, especially those they see at Mass (musicians, ushers, lectors, etc.) and their own catechists, but they may not be fully aware of what these people do or why. We can help children this age understand the jobs of these special "helpers" by explaining in simple, child-friendly language.

Visit **Allelu.com** for weekly Scripture readings, reflections, and activities.

The Church Prays All Year

This Week's Scripture

reminds us about how there is a time for everything and creates an understanding for the seasons in the Church year.

A Time for Everything

There is a time for everything under Heaven.
A time to plant,
A time harvest,
A time to cry,
A time to laugh,
A time to rest,
A time to work,
A time to be silent,
A time to speak.

Based on Ecclesiastes 3:1–7

Sharing Faith at Home Share the Scripture with your child by talking about its meaning or reading it aloud at bedtime. Discussion starter: What is your favorite season of the year? Why?

Through the Week

After Mass this week, talk about what color vestments the priest wore. Discuss the current Church season.

Ask Me!

Ask your child these questions, and see if he or she can give you the answers. *(If not, give a hint, and review the questions again later.)*

1. What is one thing the Church uses to mark time? *(colors)*
2. What does the color purple mean in the Church year? *(that we are "getting ready")*
3. What are the gold or white "celebration" times in the Church? *(Christmas and Easter)*

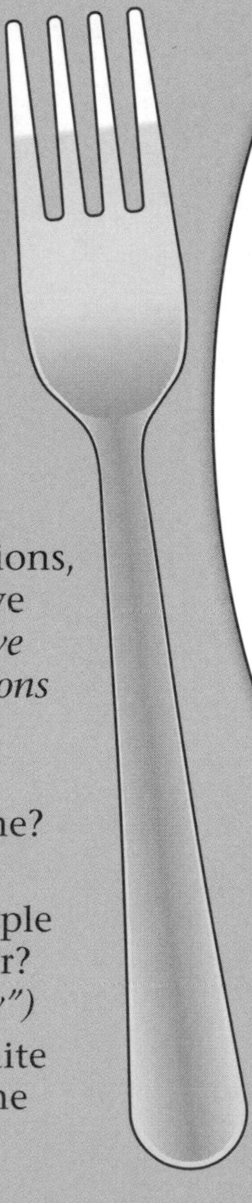

Setting the

Ho
Church

Color each prie
liturgi

Advent

Christmas

ent = purple
hristmas = white or gold

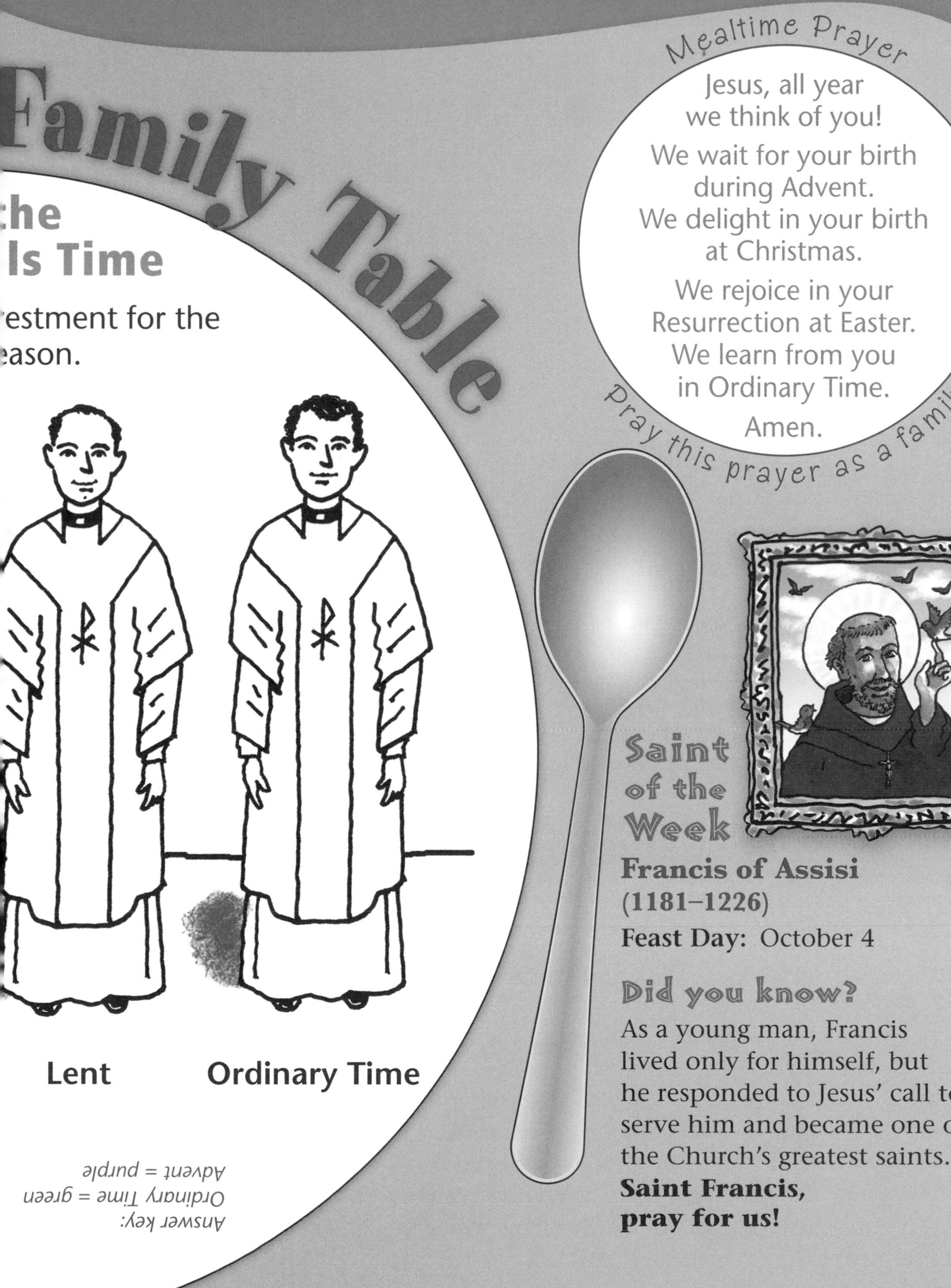

Family Table

the
ls Time

estment for the
eason.

Lent

Ordinary Time

Answer key:
Ordinary Time = green
Advent = purple

Mealtime Prayer

Jesus, all year
we think of you!
We wait for your birth
during Advent.
We delight in your birth
at Christmas.
We rejoice in your
Resurrection at Easter.
We learn from you
in Ordinary Time.
Amen.

Pray this prayer as a family.

Saint of the Week

Francis of Assisi
(1181–1226)

Feast Day: October 4

Did you know?

As a young man, Francis lived only for himself, but he responded to Jesus' call to serve him and became one of the Church's greatest saints. **Saint Francis, pray for us!**

Parent Notes

In this week's lesson your child learned

- The Church uses colors to mark time.
- The seasons of the Church year help us think about and celebrate Christ's life and work of salvation.

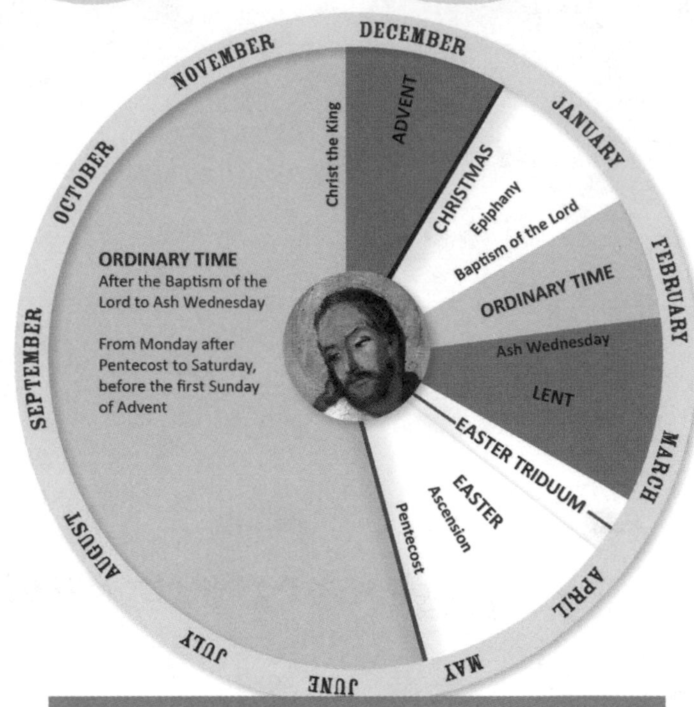

It Helps to Know

Scripture tells us that

- "There is an appointed time for everything and a time for every affair under the heavens" (Ecclesiastes 3:1).

The *Catechism* teaches us that

- the life of the Church is ordered according to seasons with Sunday as the foundation for the liturgical year. In the cycle of the Church year, we re-experience the awaiting that preceded Christ, the celebration of his Incarnation, the drama of his death, and the triumph of his Resurrection.
- just as "the presence of the Risen Lord and his saving work permeates the entire Liturgical Year" (*USCCA,* Ch. 14), through all of the seasons in our lives, God is with us.

Keep It Simple

Help your child learn about the Church year with visible symbols.

- Pray together prayers that correspond with the liturgical season.
- You may also wish to change the colors on your home's prayer table to correspond with the liturgical seasons and talk about what the colors mean.

How Four- and Five-Year-Olds Understand the Lesson, by Joseph White, Ph.D.

Time is still a mystery for young children, and they are most likely to notice the concrete, visible symbols that mark the passage of time, such as celebrations that mark particular days or seasons. Similarly, they will recognize the passage of the Church year through the change of colors in the Church décor and the vestments of the priest, and through the special liturgical celebrations.

Visit **Allelu.com** for weekly Scripture readings, reflections, and activities.

Jesus Cares for His Friends

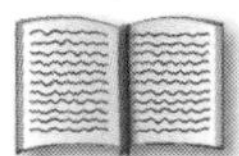

This Week's Scripture Story

reminds us that everyone has feelings, which come from God.

The Story of Lazarus

One day Jesus learned that his friend Lazarus was sick. Lazarus's sisters Martha and Mary asked Jesus to come and heal him. But when Jesus arrived, he found out that Lazarus had already died. Martha and Mary were crying, and Jesus cried with them. Jesus assured them that Lazarus would rise again. He went to the tomb where Lazarus lay, and prayed to his Father in Heaven. Then he said to Lazarus, "Come out." Lazarus did as Jesus commanded. As Jesus had promised, Lazarus was alive again.

Based on John 11:1–3, 17, 23, 32–35, 38–43

Sharing Faith at Home Share the Scripture with your child by discussing the events of the story or reading it aloud at bedtime. Discussion starter: How can you know that God always loves you?

Through the Week

Model expressing feelings in ways that show respect for others.

Ask Me!

Ask your child these questions, and see if he or she can give you the answers. *(If not, give a hint, and review the questions again later.)*

1. Where do feelings come from? *(When God created us, he made us to have many kinds of feelings.)*
2. What are some different kinds of feelings? *(happy, sad, angry, afraid, etc.)*
3. Is it okay to have different kinds of feelings? *(Yes, but when we have negative feelings, like anger or frustration, we must learn to talk about them instead of acting out.)*

Setting the

How
I I

Circle the face to show
were the pers
Then **draw** a hap

Family Table
ould
l?
v you would feel if you
n the picture.
icture of yourself.
Mealtime Prayer
God our
Father, you created
us to experience many
feelings. We can be happy,
sad, surprised, scared,
angry, or silly!
Our feelings help us show love
for others. Thank for you
giving us your Son, Jesus,
who loves us always.
Amen.
Pray this prayer as a family.
Saint of the Week
Katharine Drexel
(1889–1955)
Feast Day: March 3
Did you know?
Katharine was raised by very wealthy parents who lived their Catholic faith every day. Their example taught Katharine the importance of helping others. She worked tirelessly to provide education to those most in need.
Saint Katharine, pray for us!

Parent Notes

In this week's lesson your child learned

- God created us to have many kinds of feelings.
- It is okay to have many kinds of feelings.

It Helps to Know

Scripture tells us that

- Jesus experienced a variety of emotions, from sadness at the death of his friend Lazarus (John 11:35), to anger at the thieves who set up shop in the Temple (Matthew 21:13), to joy at God's grace at work in the minds and hearts of the simple (Luke 10:21), to almost overwhelming anxiety just before his death (Mark 14:33–36).

The *Catechism* teaches us that

- feelings can spur us to positive action or destructive behavior, depending on how we use and master them. (*CCC,* 1763)
- true love, which is wanting the best for another person, is the primary emotion and the one that can help us master all others, so that we may grow in our relationships with our friends, spouses, and children. (*CCC,* 1765–1766)

Keep It Simple

- Make sure you are mastering your own feelings and showing respect for others at home. Children tend to do what they see.
- Increase your child's "feelings" vocabulary by reflecting what you see when they are showing an emotion strongly. For example, you might say, "I can see that you're really feeling frustrated because you want to keep playing outside and I said it was time for dinner." Show some feeling in your words as you reflect these feelings, so your child can sense that you really understand how he or she feels.

How Four- and Five-Year-Olds Understand the Lesson, by Joseph White, Ph.D.

From infancy onward, most children express feelings freely, although they might not label them verbally. A major task for children is to learn to express feelings in ways that show respect for others. This will often mean learning the verbal names of feelings and practicing talking about them with words (for example, saying "I'm frustrated because ..." rather than having a tantrum).

Visit **Allelu.com** for weekly Scripture readings, reflections, and activities.

We Follow the Rules

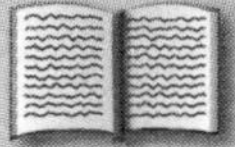

This Week's Scripture Story

helps us understand that we should listen to our parents.

Mary and Joseph Find Jesus

When Jesus was a boy, his family traveled to the city of Jerusalem. When it was time to return home, Jesus stayed behind in the Temple. He wanted to talk with the priests and teachers. On their journey, Mary and Joseph thought Jesus was with relatives who were traveling in their group. When they realized he was not, they returned to Jerusalem to look for him. They searched for Jesus for three days. When at last they found him, Mary said to him, "Why have you done this? Your father and I have been so worried." Jesus returned home with them, and was obedient to them.

Based on Luke 2:41–51

Sharing Faith at Home Share the story with your child by talking about its meaning or reading it aloud at bedtime.
Discussion starter: Why is it important to listen to your mom or dad?

Setting the

Through the Week

Talk about how the rules in your family relate to God's own rules for our lives.

Ask Me!

Ask your child these questions, and see if he or she can give you the answers. *(If not, give a hint, and review the questions again later.)*

1. Who has special jobs in a family? *(Everyone—parents and children have special jobs)*
2. What is a parent's job? *(To take care of his or her children and give them what they need)*
3. What is a child's job? *(To listen to his or her parents and follow their rules)*

W
List

Circle the child
to their mom a
pictures. **Tell** ab
your m

Family Table

Is
ing?

ho are listening
ad. **Color** those
ow you listen to
r dad.

Mealtime Prayer

Dear Jesus,
you were once a little
child who lived in a family
and had to learn many things,
just as we do.
Please help us as a family
to listen to and love
each other each day.
Amen.

Pray this prayer as a family.

Saint of the Week

Joseph (first century)
Feast Days: March 19 and May 1

Did you know?

Saint Joseph was a humble carpenter from Nazareth who was the husband of the Virgin Mary and the foster father of Jesus.

Saint Joseph, pray for us!

In this week's lesson your child learned

- Parents and children have special "jobs" in a family.
- One of the "jobs" of children is to follow their mom's and dad's rules.

It Helps to Know

Scripture tells us that

- by God's design, parents should be the first and best teachers of their children. Saint Paul emphasizes this point, saying, "Children, obey your parents in everything, for this pleases the Lord" (Ephesians 6:1).

The *Catechism* teaches us that

- God gives us rules by which to live our lives, not to burden us, but to free us to be all that we can be. "As long as a child lives at home with his parents, the child should obey his parents in all that they ask of him when it is for his good or that of the family" (*CCC,* 2217).

Keep It Simple

- Make sure your child knows what the rules are at home and in public places, and back up limits with action, rewarding good behavior by noticing and complimenting it, and imposing logical consequences for misbehavior.
- When working on specific behaviors, model the behavior you would like to see, and coach your child by practicing the behavior yourself.

How Four- and Five-Year-Olds Understand the Lesson, by Joseph White, Ph.D.

Many four- and five-year-olds make decisions about right and wrong based on a "reward and punishment orientation," meaning that they decide what to do and what not to do based on whether they will be rewarded or punished. Young children are primarily self-focused, and will often make decisions based on the utilitarian principle of "what's in it for me?" At the same time, they are beginning to understand the feelings of others and may begin to have some appreciation for the need to have "social contracts"—standards we agree on as a group that keep people safe, promote the "common good," and help us to get along with one another.

Visit **Allelu.com** for weekly Scripture readings, reflections, and activities.

We Love God and Each Other

This Week's Scripture Story

reminds us that Jesus asks us to love him with all of our feelings and all of our thinking and even all of our moving! And Jesus asks that we love each other too!

Jesus Teaches About Love

Jesus tells us that this is how we will get to Heaven: "You shall love your God with all your heart, with all your being, with all your strength, and with all your mind; and you shall love your neighbor as yourself."

Based on Luke 10:27

Sharing Faith at Home Share the Scripture with your child by talking about its meaning as a family.
Discussion starter: Name some people who God wants us to love.

Settting the

Through the Week

Think of one way someone shows love to you and one way you can show love to that person.

Ask Me!

Ask your child these questions, and see if he or she can give you the answers. *(If not, give a hint, and review the questions again later.)*

1. How does Jesus say we should love God? *(with all our heart and all our strength)*
2. Why should we love others? *(because God loves us, and tells us to love each other)*
3. What are some ways you show love to others?

W
Showi

Draw a circle around
showing love. **Dra**
someone

Family Table

Is Love?

pictures of the children **paste** a picture of ving love.

Mealtime Prayer

Dear Jesus,
we know you love us.
Every day we grow
in our love for you.
We know you want us
to love others.
Please help our family learn
to love as you do.
Amen.

Pray this prayer as a family.

Saint of the Week

John of Kanty
(1390–1473)

Feast Day: December 23

Did you know?

John of Kanty was a Polish priest, theologian, and university professor. He was known for his good humor and humility. He taught his students to treat others with kindness and love.

Saint John,
pray for us!

Parent Notes

In this week's lesson your child learned

- God loves us, and we should love others.
- We can show love to others in many different ways.

It Helps to Know

The *Catechism* teaches us that

- "Jesus makes charity the new commandment. By loving his own "to the end," he makes manifest the Father's love, which he receives. By loving one another, the disciples imitate the love of Jesus. Jesus says: "As the Father has loved me, so have I loved you; abide in my love." And again: "This is my commandment, that you love one another as I have loved you." (*CCC,* 1823)
- It has been said that charity begins at home. When we wish to grow in our ability to show love to others, it is good to begin with those who are closest to us. But we are also commanded to show love to the most vulnerable or marginalized in our society, and even to our enemies. (*CCC,* 1889)

Keep It Simple

- If your child primarily relates to others through talking, spending time talking and listening to him to him or her and showing love in verbal ways is extremely important.
- Likewise, if your child is visual learners, tokens of love that he or she can see are important. For children enjoy hands-on work and physical in interactions with others, physical touch is important.

How Four- and Five-Year-Olds Understand the Lesson, by Joseph White, Ph.D.

Love is an abstract concept, but it's one that young children understand and incorporate naturally as they form relationships with important people in their lives. They experience various expressions of love from their parents (from words of love to hugs and kisses, to help with everyday activities and basic needs), and they can also learn to show love to others in their own way, through helping others, making things for others, and in other developmentally appropriate ways.

Visit **Allelu.com** for weekly Scripture readings, reflections, and activities.

Jesus Teaches Us About Love

This Week's Scripture Story

teaches us about the importance of being kind to one another and other ways to follow Jesus' golden rule.

The Good Samaritan

To help his followers understand how we should treat other people, Jesus told this story.

"A Jewish man traveling alone was stopped by robbers. They hurt him badly and stole his money. Then they left him lying on the side of the road.

"Along came a Jewish priest. He did not help the hurt traveler.

"Then along came a Levite, a helper from the Temple. He did not care for the traveler either.

"Now a third person saw the man who was hurt. He was from Samaria. Samaritans and Jews did not get along well. But this Samaritan man put medicine on the man's wounds and bandaged them. Then he took him to an inn and paid the inn keeper to take care of him."

Jesus then explained that we must treat all people with kindness, just as the Samaritan treated the Jewish man who was hurt.

Based on Luke 10:29–37

Sharing Faith at Home Share the story with your child by talking about its meaning or reading it aloud at bedtime.
Discussion starter: Can you think of a time you helped someone?

Through the Week

Discuss how rules about sharing, taking turns, and being kind follow Jesus' command to treat others as we would like to be treated.

Ask Me!

Ask your child these questions, and see if he or she can give you the answers. *(If not, give a hint, and review the questions again later.)*

1. How did the Samaritan help the man who was hurt? *(by caring for his injuries and taking him to the inn)*
2. How did Jesus say we should treat others? *(We should treat others the way we want to be treated.)*
3. What are some ways you treat others as Jesus wants?

Setting the

Wha
Make

Match the items on th
on the right. Then **dra**
make

Family Table

Can I Share?

t with the correct item
ne more thing you can
hare.

Mealtime Prayer

Dear Jesus, help us treat each other the way we want to be treated.
When someone is hurt, let us show our love.
When someone is scared, let us show our love.
When someone is sick or tired, let us show our love. Amen.

Pray this prayer as a family.

Saint of the Week

Brigid of Ireland (450–525)

Feast Day: February 1

Did you know?

Saint Brigid is one of the patron saints of Ireland. Inspired by the preaching of Saint Patrick, she grew in faith and chose to enter religious life. She had great love for Jesus and tremendous devotion to helping the poor. **Saint Brigid, pray for us!**

Parent Notes

In this week's lesson your child learned

- Jesus said to treat others the way we want to be treated.
- We should welcome others, share with them, and take turns.

It Helps to Know

Scripture tells us that

- Jesus says to love "your neighbor as yourself" (Luke 10:27) and "treat others the way you would have them treat you" (Matthew 7:12). Jesus doesn't tell us to treat others the way they treat us, but rather how we would like them to treat us.

The *Catechism* teaches us that

- Respect for the human person proceeds by way of respect for the principle that "everyone should look upon his neighbor (without any exception) as 'another self,' above all bearing in mind his life and the means necessary for living it with dignity" (*CCC,* 1931).

Keep It Simple

- Reinforce the main points of this lesson by taking opportunities to reflect on the feelings of others. For example, while reading a story, ask your child how he or she thinks various characters are feeling.
- If you have more than one child at home, encourage them to tell each other how they are feeling, especially during conflict situations.

How Four- and Five-Year-Olds Understand the Lesson, by Joseph White, Ph.D.

The development of empathy begins in early childhood, but continues into adulthood, as we grow in our capacity to understand and respond to the feelings of others. Four- and five-year-olds tend to think the rest of the world sees the world as they do, and may often have difficulty with putting themselves in someone else's shoes. Still, children this age can learn to identify and understand the feelings of others and respond to them.

Visit **Allelu.com** for weekly Scripture readings, reflections, and activities.

God Forgives and Helps Us

This Week's Scripture Story

teaches us that it is important to say "I'm sorry" and make things right when we do something wrong.

Jesus and Zacchaeus

Zacchaeus collected money from people for taxes. Sometimes he took more money than he was supposed to and kept it for himself.

When Jesus was traveling through Zacchaeus's town, Zacchaeus wanted to see him. He climbed a sycamore tree to better see Jesus.

When Jesus reached the tree, he said to Zacchaeus, "Come down quickly, for today I must stay at your house."

At supper, Zacchaeus asked Jesus for forgiveness. He also promised to repay the people he had stolen from.

Jesus reassured Zacchaeus that he was forgiven. He said to him, "Today salvation has come to this house."

Based on Luke 19:1–10

Sharing Faith at Home Share the story with your child by talking about its meaning or reading it aloud at bedtime.
Discussion starter: When have you said "sorry" to someone?

Through the Week

Foster loving actions by spending one-on-one time this week listening, playing a game, and sharing other experiences as a family.

Ask Me!

Ask your child these questions, and see if he or she can give you the answers. *(If not, give a hint, and review the questions again later.)*

1. How did Jesus treat Zacchaeus? *(With forgiveness; he had dinner at his home.)*
2. Does God love us even when we make wrong choices? *(Yes, God always loves us.)*
3. What should we do when we have done something wrong? *(We should say we are sorry, and work to make things better.)*

Setting the

M... Good

Mark an X on the ... wrong choices. **Circle t**... good choices. **Tell** ... you h...

Family Table

ng
hoices

ren who are making
hildren who are making
t the good choices
made.

Mealtime Prayer

Jesus,
sometimes we fight,
and don't share.
Sometimes we are
not good listeners.

But you love us when
we are good and when
we can do better.

Thank you for
loving us always!

Amen.

Pray this prayer as a family.

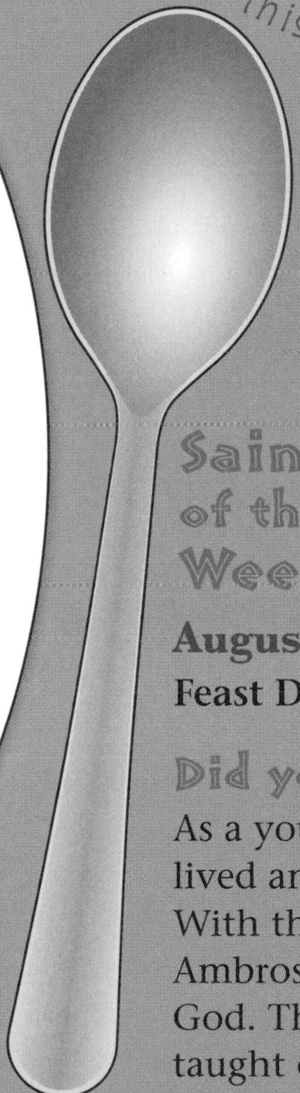

Saint of the Week

Augustine (354–430)

Feast Day: August 28

Did you know?

As a young man, Augustine lived an immoral life. With the guidance of Saint Ambrose, he came to know God. Through his writings he taught countless people about God. He became one of the Church's greatest saints.

Saint Augustine, pray for us!

Parent Notes

In this week's lesson your child learned

- God loves me always, even when I make a bad choice.
- When I do something that is wrong, I should say, "I'm sorry," and try to help make things right.

It Helps to Know

The *Catechism* teaches us that

- God created us to do good things, but we all stray from God's plan. God reaches out to us in love and calls us back to himself. God meets us in the Sacrament of Penance and Reconciliation, pouring out his mercy and granting us forgiveness. God also asks us to participate with him in repairing the damage done by our unloving actions.
- "Many sins wrong our neighbor. One must do what is possible in order to repair the harm (return stolen goods, restore the reputation of someone slandered, pay compensation for injuries). Simple justice requires as much" (*CCC,* 1459).

Keep It Simple

- As a family, take time to name blessings in your life. Talk about good things that have happened this week, material goods you are grateful for, and people in your life for whom you are thankful, and material goods you are grateful for.
- Discuss ways to show gratitude to God, such as through responsible use of what you are given, prayers of thanksgiving, and sharing with others.

How Four- and Five-Year-Olds Understand the Lesson, by Joseph White, Ph.D.

Four- and five-year-olds are still learning the rules and guidelines given to them by parents and others who care for them. Your child will learn about the unconditional love of God as he or she experiences your unconditional love, and that will motivate him or her to make good choices.

Because preschool children are developmentally egocentric, they often have little insight into how their actions affect others, but they can begin to grow in empathy as they listen to others express how they feel.

Visit **Allelu.com** for weekly Scripture readings, reflections, and activities.

We Learn to Forgive

This Week's Scripture Story

reminds us that we must always forgive others.

Forgiving Each Other

Jesus spoke to his Apostles about how we must forgive.

He said to them, "When someone hurts you in some way, go and find the person, and talk quietly about what happened. If the person will not listen to you, ask others to help the person understand how he or she was hurtful."

Peter said to Jesus, "Lord, if someone insults me or hurts me in some way, how many times must I forgive him? Must I forgive him seven times?" Jesus replied, "Not seven times, but seventy-seven times."

Based on Matthew 18:15–16, 21–22

Sharing Faith at Home Share the story with your child by talking about its meaning or reading it aloud at bedtime. Discussion starter: When have you forgiven someone?

Through the Week

Encourage each member of your family to act as a peacemaker. Invite each person to share what he or she has done.

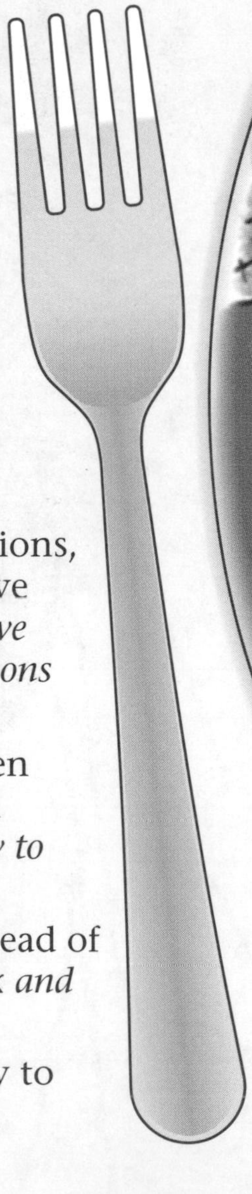

Ask Me!

Ask your child these questions, and see if he or she can give you the answers. *(If not, give a hint, and review the questions again later.)*

1. What should we do when we have a problem with someone? *(We should try to make peace.)*

2. What should we do instead of fighting? *(We should talk and try to forgive.)*

3. What is one way you try to make peace?

Setting the

How
Be Pea

Circle then **color** th
peacemakers. Then **t**
children can

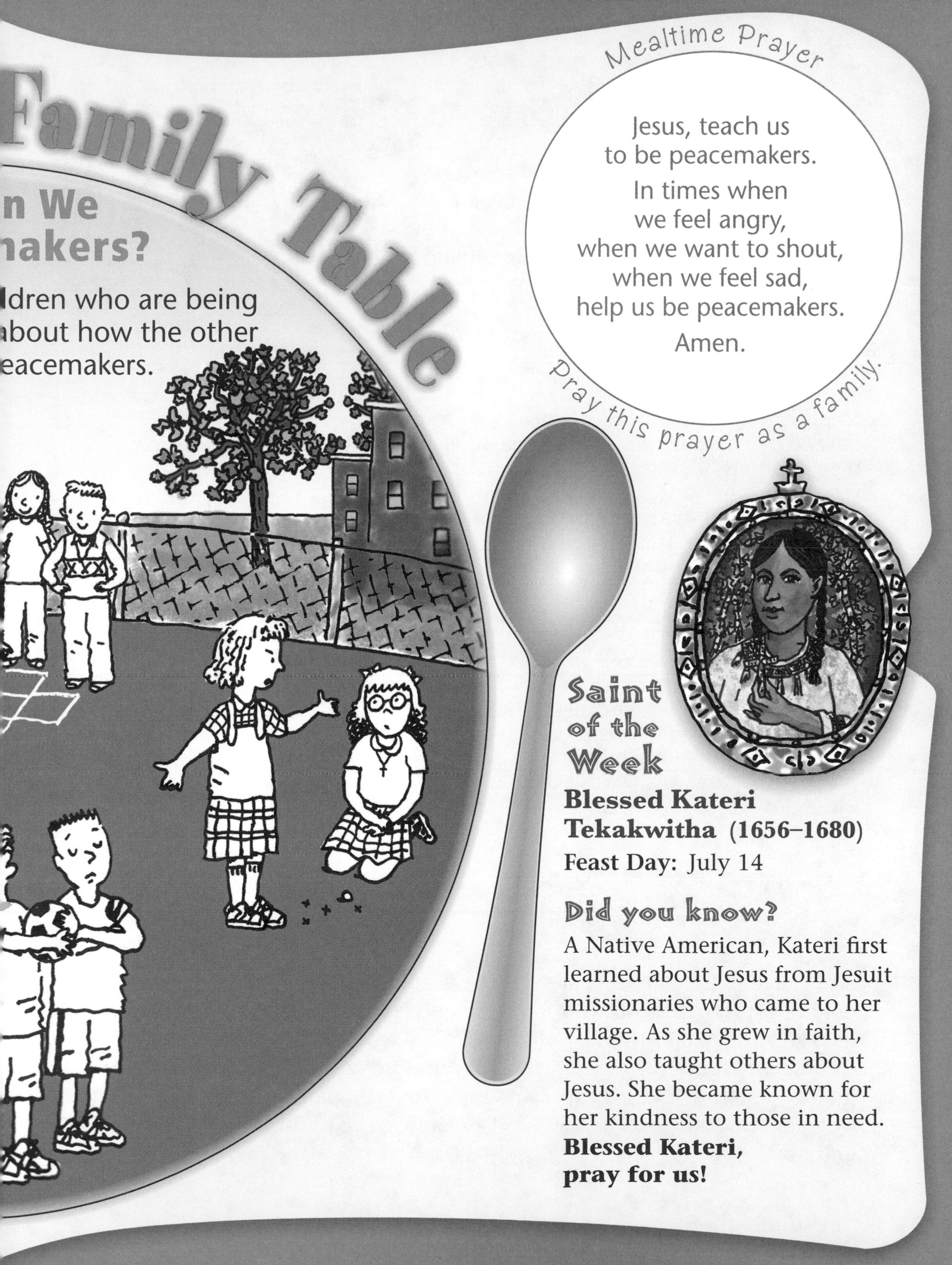

Family Table

n We
nakers?

ldren who are being
about how the other
eacemakers.

Mealtime Prayer

Jesus, teach us
to be peacemakers.
In times when
we feel angry,
when we want to shout,
when we feel sad,
help us be peacemakers.
Amen.

Pray this prayer as a family.

Saint of the Week

Blessed Kateri Tekakwitha (1656–1680)

Feast Day: July 14

Did you know?

A Native American, Kateri first learned about Jesus from Jesuit missionaries who came to her village. As she grew in faith, she also taught others about Jesus. She became known for her kindness to those in need.

Blessed Kateri, pray for us!

Parent Notes

In this week's lesson your child learned

- When we have a problem with someone, we should try to make peace.
- When we disagree with others, we should talk instead of fighting.

It Helps to Know

Scripture tells us that

- we should try to overcome conflicts we have, either on our own or by seeking the help of others. Jesus said to his disciples: "If your brother sins against you, go and tell him his fault between you and him alone. If he listens to you, you have won over your brother. If he does not listen, take one or two others along with you." (See Matthew 18:15–20.)

The *Catechism* teaches us that

- when we forgive others, we follow Christ: "Christian prayer extends to the forgiveness of enemies, transfiguring the disciple by configuring him to his Master. Forgiveness also bears witness that, in our world, love is stronger than sin" (*CCC,* 2844).

Keep It Simple

- When your child is frustrated, angry, or upset, try the "1-2-3-check" method. Ask these questions: "What is the problem?" (Step 1), "What are your choices?" (Step 2), "Which action will you take?" (Step 3), and "How did it work?" (Check). Over time, your child will learn to mentally go through these steps on his or her own.
- Model the right way to handle conflict by showing patience and reason with your child when he or she acts out or misbehaves.

How Four- and Five-Year-Olds Understand the Lesson, by Joseph White, Ph.D.

The early childhood years are a time of rapid language growth. Kids are learning how to use words instead of fighting, and at times, they push, hit, and kick. They do this even when they have learned better ways of handling conflicts because they are still growing in their capacity for impulse control. In fact, the part of the brain responsible for "stopping to think" before acting will continue to grow throughout the childhood years and is not fully mature until one is in his or her early twenties.

Visit **Allelu.com** for weekly Scripture readings, reflections, and activities.

We Wait for Jesus with Joy

This Week's Scripture Story

helps us learn how Mary and Joseph were a part of God's plan to send his Son.

The Angel Announces Jesus' Birth

God sent the angel Gabriel to Mary in Nazareth. The angel said to her, "Greetings, Mary! The Lord is with you!"

Mary was worried. Why had an angel come to her?

"Do not be afraid," Gabriel said to her. "God has chosen you to be the mother of his Son."

Mary answered, "I will do what God asks."

Gabriel later spoke to Joseph in a dream, "Do not be afraid. Mary's child is the Son of God. You are to take care of Mary. And when the child is born, you are to name him Jesus." Joseph did as the angel asked.

All this happened because God promised to send his Son.

Based on Luke 1:26–35, 38 and Matthew 1:19–21, 24

Sharing Faith at Home Share the story with your child by talking about its meaning or reading it aloud at bedtime.
Discussion starter: How can you show your love for God, as Mary did?

Through the Week

Look for symbols of promises. Some examples include wedding rings, arm bands, and rainbows.

Ask Me!

Ask your child these questions, and see if he or she can give you the answers. *(If not, give a hint, and review the questions again later.)*

1. What is a promise? *(saying you will do something)*
2. What promise did God make long ago? *(that he would send his Son)*
3. Did God keep his promise? *(Yes. God always keeps his promises!)*

Setting the

The
Visit

Look at the
Find and **circle** eac
Color Mary and t

Family Table
ngel
Mary
s in the box.
these in the picture.
rchangel Gabriel.
Mealtime Prayer
Thank you,
our Father in Heaven,
for sending us your Son, Jesus.
We praise for your goodness
and thank you for
keeping your promises.
Amen.
Pray this prayer as a family.
Saint of the Week
Nicholas (c. 280–343)
Feast Day: December 6
Did you know?
Nicholas came from a wealthy family. As a young man, he gave away his money to help people in need. He became a priest, and then a bishop. He often performed secret acts of kindness.
Saint Nicholas,
pray for us!

Parent Notes

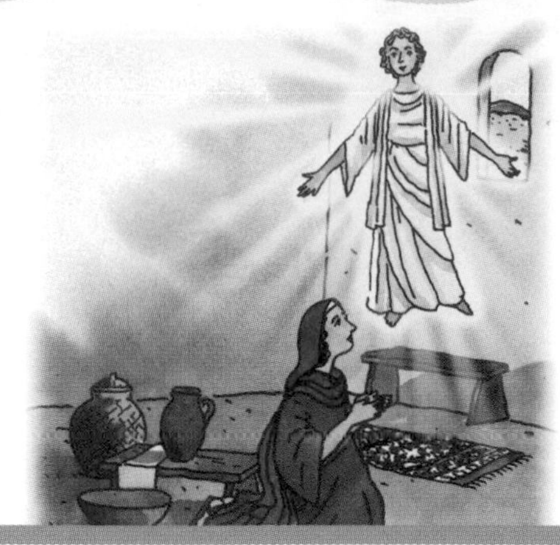

In this week's lesson your child learned

- Making a promise means saying you will do something.
- God promised to send his Son, and he kept his promise.

It Helps to Know

Scripture tells us that

- the writer of Hebrews discusses great heroes of faith, such as Abraham and Moses, who believed in God's promises even before they were seen. This text describes faith as "the realization of what is hoped for and evidence of things not seen" (Hebrews 11:1).

The *Catechism* teaches us that

- throughout history, God has gradually revealed himself to his people as they are ready to hear and understand his message. The *Catechism states,* "God communicates himself to man gradually. He prepares him to welcome by stages the supernatural Revelation that is to culminate in the person and mission of the Incarnate Word, Jesus Christ" (*CCC,* 53).

Keep It Simple

- Children are still learning about promises and trust, and their relationship with their parents is the first and most important place trust is established. Help your child always take you at your word by taking care never to be too casual about making promises to your child.
- Point out the connections between what is said and what is done by you and other family members (including the children), emphasizing that you strive to mean what you say and to do what you promise.

How Four- and Five-Year-Olds Understand the Lesson, by Joseph White, Ph.D.

Young children often use the word "promise" casually, saying "I promise" to mean "I am really telling the truth." Conversely, they take the words of significant adults very seriously, and when plans change or adults change their minds, they might say, "But you promised...." Children this age are still learning what it means to give one's word and keep it, but they can begin to understand the concept of a God who always does what he says he will do—a God who keeps his promises.

Visit **Allelu.com** for weekly Scripture readings, reflections, and activities.

Jesus Came for All People

This Week's Scripture Story

tells us about the shepherds whom the angels invited to the place of Jesus' birth.

The Shepherds' Surprise

In the fields outside of Bethlehem, shepherds kept watch over their sheep in the dark night. Suddenly an angel surrounded by a bright light appeared to them. The shepherds were afraid.

The angel said, "Don't fear. I bring happy news for you and for all people! In Bethlehem a baby has been born who is the Son of God. You will find the baby lying in a manger."

Then the shepherds were surrounded by many, many angels! These angels sang, "Glory to God in the highest!"

The angels then left to go back to God.

The shepherds said to one another, "Let us go to Bethlehem." And they hurried to Bethlehem, where they found Mary and Joseph and the baby Jesus. The shepherds told many other people along the way about the angels' message.

As the shepherds walked back to the fields, they praised God for all the wonder and joy of this holy night.

Based on Luke 2:8–20

Sharing Faith at Home Help your child recall the Scripture by acting out the story together.

Discussion starter: How do you tell people about Jesus?

Through the Week

Each evening, discuss one way each of you can share the good news of God's love.

Ask Me!

Ask your child these questions, and see if he or she can give you the answers. *(If not, give a hint, and review the questions again later.)*

1. Whom did the angels invite to meet the baby Jesus? *(shepherds)*
2. Why did God welcome the shepherds to Jesus' birth? *(to show that Jesus came for everyone)*
3. How might the shepherds have felt when they saw the baby Jesus?

Setting the

The First

Draw a line to match the pictures on the rig the Christmas sto

Family Table

hristmas

ictures from the left to
/ith your family, **retell**
your own words.

Mealtime Prayer

Dear God, our Father,
thank you for sending
us your Son!
We praise you for this
wonderful gift at
Christmas and always.
Glory to God in the highest!
Amen.

Pray this prayer as a family.

Saint of the Week

Vincent de Paul
(1580–1660)
Feast Day: September 27

Did you know?

Vincent de Paul was a priest in France at a time when some people were very wealthy and most were very poor. He dedicated his life to helping the poor.

Saint Vincent de Paul, pray for us!

In this week's lesson your child learned

- The angels invited poor shepherds to meet Baby Jesus.
- God welcomed the shepherds to Jesus' birth to show that Jesus came for everyone—especially the poor.

It Helps to Know

The *Catechism* teaches us that

- through the grace of theSacrament of Marriage, parents receive the responsibility and privilege of evangelizing their children. Parents should initiate their children at an early age into the mysteries of the faith for which they are "first heralds" for their children. (*CCC*, 2225)

Keep It Simple

- Let your child see you making efforts to welcome others in the community, at home, and in the parish.
- One "welcoming" activity that is particularly relevant to this theme is the "Gabriel Project," a program in which the parish provides for basic needs for young and/or single mothers. If you participate in this or a similar outreach, your child can help you shop for supplies to bring to donate.

How Four- and Five-Year-Olds Understand the Lesson, by Joseph White, Ph.D.

Children are naturally full of hope, and tend to dream big. They enjoy stories that foreshadow great things to come. For these reasons, children are excited by the story of the angels' announcement of Jesus' birth. Young children also enjoy sharing things they are excited about, and can naturally share the good news of God's love when given opportunities. What is sometimes less intuitive for them, though, is the idea of outreach to the poor. This is to be expected, because of their limited experience with the world.

Visit **Allelu.com** for weekly Scripture readings, reflections, and activities.

Our Lenten Walk with Jesus

This Week's Scripture Story

focuses on the events of the Last Supper.

At the Last Supper

On the night before he died, Jesus was having his last meal with the Apostles. Before they ate, Jesus poured water into a basin and washed the Apostles' feet. He wiped them dry with a towel.

Jesus explained to the Apostles that he did this to set an example for them. He said, "As I treat you, you must treat one another."

Then Jesus took bread, blessed it, and broke it. He gave the bread to his friends and said, "This is my body, which will be given for you. Do this in memory of me."

After they had eaten, he took the cup and said, "This is my blood. It will be shed for you."

Based on John 13:1–15 and Luke 22:14–20

Sharing Faith at Home Share the Scripture with your child by reading the story aloud at mealtime and talking about the events. Discussion starter: What are some things Jesus did at the Last Supper?

Through the Week

Start each day with a family reminder to do one extra kind thing for someone—at home, at preschool, or at work—that day.

Ask Me!

Ask your child these questions, and see if he or she can give you the answers. *(If not, give a hint, and review the questions again later.)*

1. What did Jesus do with his friends the night before he died? *(He shared a special meal with them and he washed their feet.)*
2. Why did Jesus wash the Apostles' feet? *(to teach them that we must all love and care for one another)*
3. Did Jesus do the things God the Father asked him to do, even though they were hard? *(Yes.)*

Setting the

A
Last

Circle the things that w
where Jesus and the Ap
Choose one of the ite
it was part o

Family Table

...e ...pper

... have been in the room ...es had the Last Supper. ...ou circled and **tell** how ... Last Supper.

Mealtime Prayer

Dear Jesus,
you showed us that we should help one another.
Give us the courage to follow your example, and help us grow in our love for you.
Amen.

Pray this prayer as a family.

Saint of the Week

Peter Claver (1581–1654)

Feast Day: September 9

Did you know?

Peter Claver, a Spanish Jesuit priest, spent more than thirty years in Cartagena (modern Colombia) ministering to the Africans brought there aboard the slave ships. He dedicated his life to this work and to fighting against the sin of slavery.

Saint Peter Claver, pray for us!

Parent Notes

In this week's lesson your child learned

- Before he died on the Cross, Jesus shared a special meal with his friends.
- Even though he was afraid, Jesus wanted to do what God the Father asked him to do.

It Helps to Know

Scripture tells us that

- at the Last Supper, Jesus began by washing the feet of his disciples, humbling himself and taking the role of a servant at the Passover meal.
- as he celebrated the Passover with his disciples, Jesus offered himself as the new Paschal Lamb who would be sacrificed to save all people, saying, "This is my body, which will be given up for you.... This cup is the new covenant" (Luke 22:19–20).

Keep It Simple

- As a family, go to Holy Thursday Mass. This will be a great opportunity for your child to see the Scripture he or she has learned "come to life."
- Discuss ways to serve others, just as Jesus washed the Apostles' feet. Name specific examples of ways family members can "serve" one another.

How Four- and Five-Year-Olds Understand the Lesson, by Joseph White, Ph.D.

While four- and five-year-olds generally cannot grasp the concept of transubstantiation, they can understand that Jesus shared a special meal with his disciples that we continue to celebrate today in the Mass. They are also capable of understanding how Jesus served his disciples in the washing of the feet and the fear Jesus felt when he knew he was about to die. With children this age, we can say, "Jesus was afraid, but he wanted to do what God the Father wanted him to do."

Visit **Allelu.com** for weekly Scripture readings, reflections, and activities.

Jesus Is Risen!

This Week's Scripture Story

focuses on Jesus' death and Resurrection.

The Resurrection

It was dawn when Jesus' friends, Mary Magdalene and another woman named Mary, went to the tomb where Jesus' body had been laid. It was the third day after Jesus had died. Guards stood nearby.

Suddenly, there was an earthquake and an angel of the Lord appeared! The angel rolled the huge stone away from the tomb entrance.

The guards were frightened and fell to the ground.

The angel turned to the women and said, "Do not be afraid. I know that you are looking for Jesus. He has been raised from the dead! Come and see the empty tomb where his body had been laid. Then go tell Jesus' other friends."

The women still felt a bit afraid, but they were also filled with joy. On their way to tell the other disciples the good news, they saw Jesus. They kneeled before him. He said to them, "Do not be afraid. Go and tell the disciples that they too will see me."

Based on Matthew 28:1–10

Sharing Faith at Home Share the Scripture with your child by talking about its meaning or reading it aloud at bedtime. Discussion starter: How would you feel if you saw the Risen Jesus?

Through the Week

Especially during the Easter season, include in your home both images of the crucified Jesus and images of the Risen Christ.

Ask Me!

Ask your child these questions, and see if he or she can give you the answers. *(If not, give a hint, and review them again later.)*

1. On what day did Jesus die on the Cross? *(Good Friday)*
2. What happened on Easter Sunday? *(Jesus rose from the dead.)*
3. How do you think the women who discovered that Jesus had risen felt?

Setting the

On
Mo

Color the scene tha
Easter morning. **Col**
yellow or gold. **Talk** w
happen

Family Table

...ster ...ing

...s what happened on ...e word "Alleluia" in ...our family about what ...n Easter.

Mealtime Prayer

Easter Prayer

Jesus, our friend, our brother, our Lord,
we are sad when we think about your death, but we are filled with joy that you rose from the dead! We thank you and we praise you!
Alleluia! Amen!

Pray this prayer as a family.

Saint of the Week

Mary Magdalene
(first century)
Feast Day: July 22

Did you know?

Mary Magdalene was one of Jesus' most faithful followers and was at the foot of the Cross when he died. She was with the disciples who discovered the empty tomb on the day of Jesus' Resurrection.

Saint Mary Magdalene, pray for us!

Parent Notes

In this week's lesson your child learned

- Jesus died on the Cross on Good Friday.
- Jesus rose from the dead on Easter Sunday.

It Helps to Know

Scripture tells us that

- through our baptism, we are united to the death and Resurrection of Jesus. We die to sin, are "buried" in the waters of Baptism, and rise again to new life. (See Romans 6:4.)

The *Catechism* teaches us that

- Jesus allowed himself to suffer and die for us, but death could not hold him, and he rose from the grave on Easter Sunday.
- in the celebration of Baptism, a priest or deacon pours water over the head of the person being baptized and says, "I baptize you in the name of the Father, and of the Son, and of the Holy Spirit." When we are joined with the Paschal Mystery in Baptism, we are adopted as sons and daughters of God. (*CCC,* 1265)

Keep It Simple

- This Easter, find ways that your family can express joy that Jesus is alive and continues to live with us and in us.
- Reflect on how Jesus' suffering and our sadness on Good Friday leads to the joy of Jesus' Resurrection on Easter Sunday.

How Four- and Five-Year-Olds Understand the Lesson, by Joseph White, Ph.D.

Death is a difficult concept for preschool children, who are still learning the laws of cause and effect and may still view death as something temporary. For this reason, children this age may easily accept the story of Jesus' Resurrection, and may not be too surprised by it. However, as they grow older and better understand the laws of nature and the permanence of death, they will gain increased appreciation of the magnitude of the Resurrection miracle.

Visit **Allelu.com** for weekly Scripture readings, reflections, and activities.

Jesus Returns to Heaven

This Week's Scripture Story

tells about Jesus ascending to Heaven forty days after his Resurrection.

Jesus Returns to His Father

Jesus had been with the disciples for many days since his Resurrection. It was now time for him to leave them.

Jesus led his disciples to a place called Bethany. He raised his hands and blessed them.

As he blessed them, he was lifted up to Heaven.

The disciples praised him and returned to Jerusalem with joy in their hearts. They spent much time in prayer, praising God.

Based on Luke 24:50–53

Sharing Faith at Home Share the story with your child by talking about its meaning or reading it aloud at bedtime.
Discussion starter: How do we know Jesus is always with us?

Through the Week

Take out some photos or videos of family members who live far away and talk about ways they are still close to you and part of your life.

Ask Me!

Ask your child these questions, and see if he or she can give you the answers. *(If not, give a hint, and review the questions again later.)*

1. What can friends do when they move far away from each other? *(They can still be friends and remember one another.)*
2. Is Jesus with us today? *(Yes, Jesus is with us, especially when we remember him.)*
3. How do you think the disciples felt when Jesus left them?

Setting the

Jesus
to

Use the code to finc
about what is ha

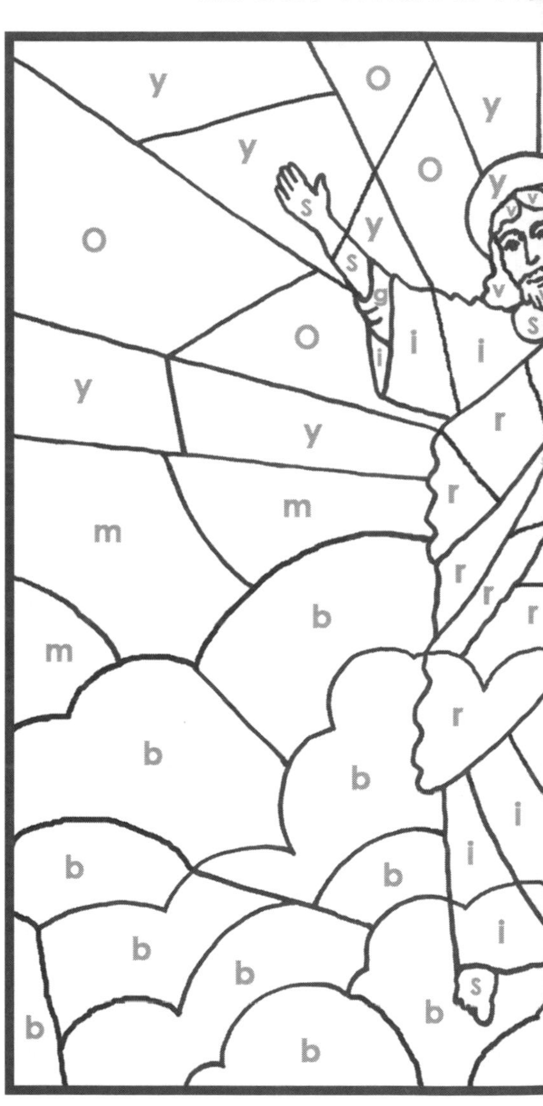

C

b = blue g = green

i = gray s = brown

cends
ven

hidden picture. **Talk**
ng in the picture.

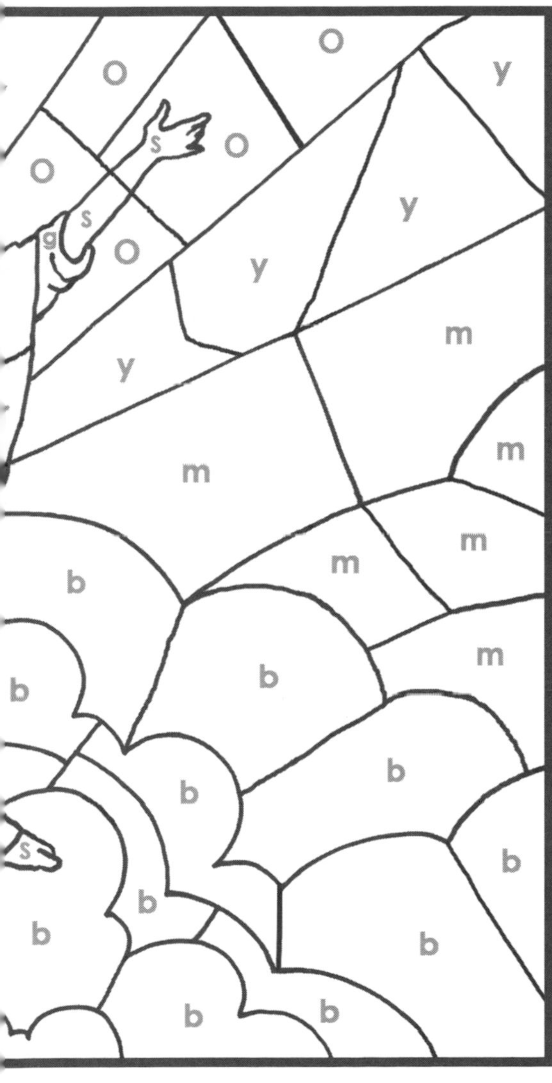

ode
nge v = black r = red
ple y = yellow

Mealtime Prayer

Dear Jesus,
we know you are near us,
and that you love us
and guide us.
Thank you for being
with us every day.
We love you
and we praise you.
Amen.

Pray this prayer as a family.

Saint of the Week

John the Apostle
(first century)
Feast Day: December 27

Did you know?

Saint John the Apostle and Evangelist, was perhaps the youngest of Jesus' Apostles. He wrote the Gospel of John, in which he emphasized Jesus' divinity and Jesus' teaching that we must all love one another.
Saint John, pray for us!

Parent Notes

In this week's lesson your child learned

- Sometimes good friends have to be apart, but they can still be friends and remember one another.
- Jesus is with us, especially when we remember him.

It Helps to Know

Scripture tells us that

- even though Jesus had prepared the Apostles for his Ascension into Heaven, they likely felt they were not ready to say goodbye (Acts 1:4–11).

The *Catechism* teaches us that

- the time children spend with their parents is an "apprenticeship in the preconditions of all true freedom" (*CCC,* 2223). To live as truly free adults, they must learn to master their own will, to exercise good judgment, and to put off what they want for what they need.

Keep It Simple

- On the way to Mass, talk about how Jesus is with us when we gather as a parish community to celebrate the Eucharist.
- Remind your child that Jesus is with us as we go about our lives each day.

How Four- and Five-Year-Olds Understand the Lesson, by Joseph White, Ph.D.

Although they sometimes protest it, even four- and five-year-olds understand that all good things must end. They have to say goodbye to play dates, go to sleep after a good bedtime story, or go back home after a fun day at the beach. A much more abstract concept for children this age is the idea that Jesus continues to be with us through the Eucharist and through his Holy Spirit. While this is difficult to convey to children this age, the point is so important that we must attempt to at least give them "hints" about this for future understanding.

The Holy Spirit Helps the Church

This Week's Scripture Story

tells about the first Pentecost. This day is also known as the day the work of the Church began.

The Day the Holy Spirit Came

Peter and the other Apostles were in Jerusalem, along with Mary, the mother of Jesus, and crowds of other people from many places. They were all celebrating a Jewish holiday called Pentecost.

Suddenly, the disciples heard a sound like a strong wind. Then they saw what looked like small flames, resting on them but without hurting them! They were filled with the Holy Spirit, which Jesus had promised to send. Now they began to speak in languages they did not know, so that all those in the crowds outside could understand them all. The people were amazed.

Peter said to the people, "Be baptized in the name of Jesus, and you will receive the Holy Spirit."

Hundreds and hundreds of people came to the Apostles to be baptized.

Based on Acts 1:14, 2:1–11, 38–41

Sharing Faith at Home Help your child understand the Scripture by reading it aloud as a family and discussing the events. Discussion starter: What amazing things happened at Pentecost?

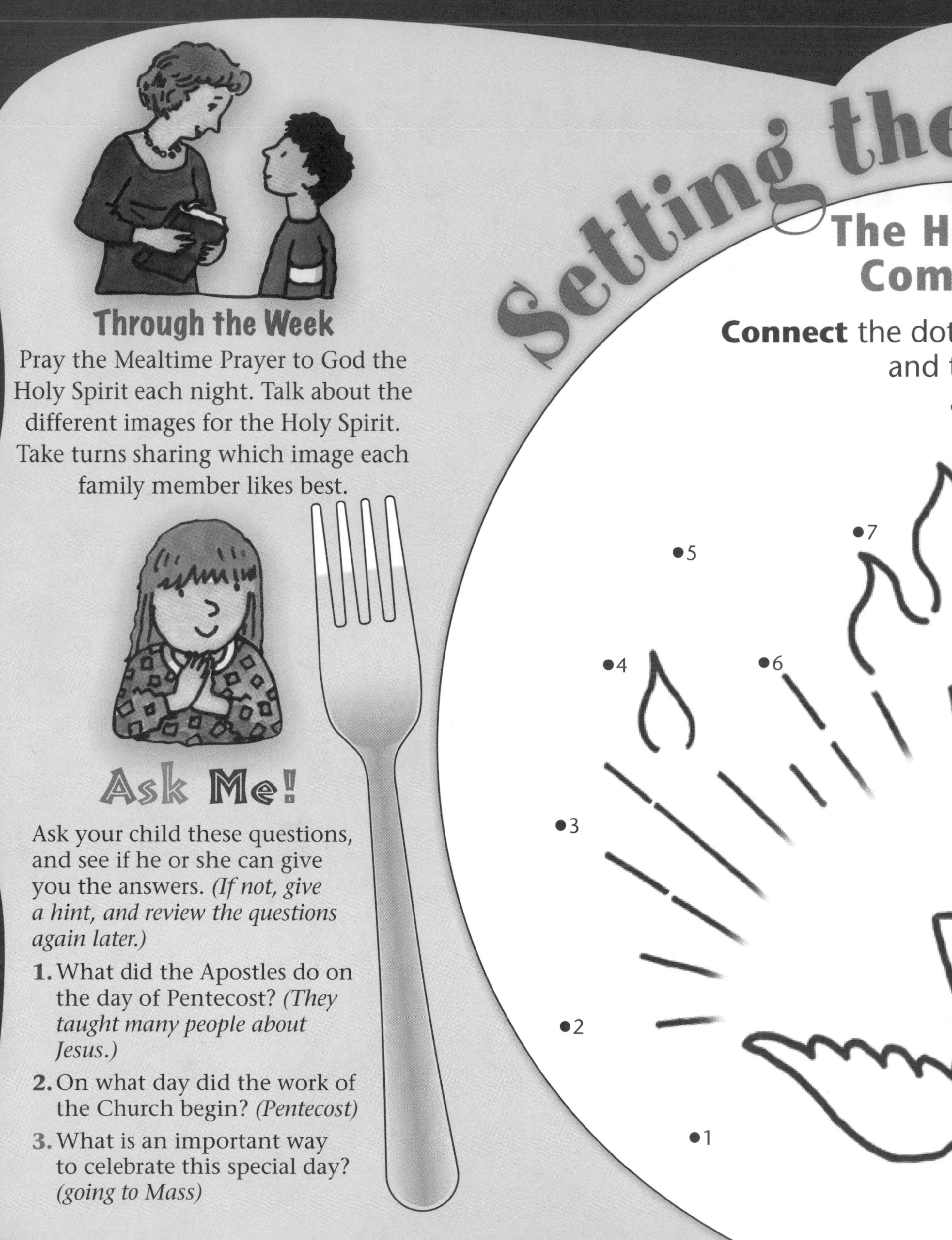

Through the Week

Pray the Mealtime Prayer to God the Holy Spirit each night. Talk about the different images for the Holy Spirit. Take turns sharing which image each family member likes best.

Ask Me!

Ask your child these questions, and see if he or she can give you the answers. *(If not, give a hint, and review the questions again later.)*

1. What did the Apostles do on the day of Pentecost? *(They taught many people about Jesus.)*
2. On what day did the work of the Church begin? *(Pentecost)*
3. What is an important way to celebrate this special day? *(going to Mass)*

Mealtime Prayer

Come to us,
Holy Spirit!
Come like a gentle dove,
so we will know God's love!
Come like a brisk wind, so we
will know God's greatness!
Come like a warming fire, so
we will know God's wisdom!
Come to us, Holy Spirit!
Amen.

Pray this prayer as a family.

Saint of the Week

Peter the Apostle
(first century)
Feast Days: June 29,
February 22

Did you know?

Jesus called Simon and his brother Andrew to follow him and be "fishers of men." Jesus later changed Simon's name to Peter, meaning "rock," and made him the leader of all the Apostles and of his Church on earth.

Saint Peter,
pray for us!

Parent Notes

In this week's lesson your child learned

- On the day of Pentecost, the Apostles taught many people about Jesus.
- Pentecost is often referred to as the day the work of the Church began.

It Helps to Know

Scripture tells us that

- in the story of Pentecost (Acts 2:1–47), Jewish people from all over the known world gathered in Jerusalem for a special feast day. With Mary present, Peter and the other Apostles began to teach them about Jesus Christ.
- each person gathered to hear the Apostles, regardless of his or her own language and dialect, heard and understood them. In response, 3,000 people were baptized that day.

Keep It Simple

Spend some time getting to know the "language" of your child by observing and reflecting as he or she plays or engages in a high-interest activity. Don't guide the play or activity; instead, observe and talk about what you are seeing (e.g., "I see the dolls in the dollhouse are gathering around the table for a meal" or "I see you are using many bright colors in that picture").

How Four- and Five-Year-Olds Understand the Lesson, by Joseph White, Ph.D.

The story of Pentecost, with its focus on miracles and the Apostles' ability to speak about Christ and be understood by all, including those who spoke other languages, may be difficult for young children to grasp. However, they are quite familiar with new beginnings, and they can understand that Pentecost is the day the work of the Church began. It is the first day that Jesus' friends shared the Good News about his life, and many, many people decided to become part of the Church that day.

Visit **Allelu.com** for weekly Scripture readings, reflections, and activities.